Science as a Superpower:

MY LIFELONG FIGHT AGAINST DISEASE AND THE HEROES WHO MADE IT POSSIBLE

By
William A. Haseltine, PhD
YOUNG READERS EDITION

"If I may offer advice to the young laboratory worker, it would be this: never neglect an extraordinary appearance or happening."

— **Alexander Fleming**

CONTENTS

Science as A Superpower!

When you think about superpowers and superheroes, certain images may come to mind: big red capes, fast cars, suits of armor, and maybe some flying around the night sky. But do you ever think about *science?* Science is the most powerful superpower in the world. If you every had any doubt about that fact, just think about COVID-19. Those masks that are protecting you from getting sick? The vaccines that your teachers and grandparents received? The drugs that doctors are giving to patients in the hospital? All that comes from *science*.

When people hear the word *science* they often think about men and women in white lab coats, pouring liquids from one test tube into the next. That's part of it. But it's more than just fun lab work that makes up science.

When rumors about a new flu-like illness started to spread in late 2019, scientists started asking the big questions: *Why* are so many more people getting sick this year? *What* is causing the sickness? *How* does the sickness spread? Eventually, they found the answers to those questions. They discovered a new type of coronavirus (something they later named SARS-CoV-2) that caused this new disease, COVID-19. Then the scientists asked more questions: *How* does the virus enter our body? *Where* does it spread once it gets inside? *Who* is most likely to get infected? *How* does the virus make us sick? Every time they found an answer to one question, they asked another. That's how the power of science works.

When you get right down to it, science is about asking big questions and then working hard to find the answer.

We've lost a lot of people to this disease—too many—but without those scientists, their questions, and their work to find the answers, hundreds of millions more could have died. *Science* is what is saving us. Now that's a superpower. The world is threatened by a terrifying new disease, but the power of science swoops in to save us.

Scientists make discoveries, heal the sick, answer (and ask!) life-changing questions and, in the process, defy all expectations of what is possible. But the best thing about science, if you ask me, is that we can *all* possess its power. We can *all* be superheroes. With the power of science, you can save the lives of the people you love…you can save the *world*.

When I was very young, I knew I wanted to seize this power. I was just four-years-old when my mother got sick. Seeing her weak in bed made me feel helpless, afraid, and anxious. And I felt too small to *do* anything, which made me incredibly frustrated. *Why is she suffering and how can I help? Is there anything I can *actually* do?* These questions were a near-constant refrain in my mind. Fortunately, my mother survived that first bout of illness but as I grew up, she became sick more and more often. Grappling with my mom's illnesses—as well as my own dips in and out of good health—I began to form a plan: I would pursue a life of healing and I would make a difference to human health. At first, I thought this meant I'd become a doctor; as a doctor I could *help*; as a doctor I could *actually do.* Later in life, however, after years of studying and collaborating with great minds, I discovered I could make an even bigger difference to health through a career in medical science.

This is why I'm writing this book: I want you to know that if you want to make a difference, if you want to help and learn and *do* something with all those competing, confusing emotions, science is your golden ticket. Science offers a unique opportunity for one person to improve human life for all time. A single person can unravel a mystery that can save millions of lives. No matter your age or gender or favorite color, no matter your family background, where you live, or what kind of grades you get in school, anyone can be a scientist. Anyone can be a hero. Science values curiosity and opens a pathway to a wonderful life: a life of meaning, of travel, of faithful friends and inspirational colleagues, of business and philanthropy and of political impact. Science is a path for students of every kind.

Science offers a unique opportunity for one person to improve human life for all time.

I wish I'd known this back when I was in the fourth grade and…flunking. I can still feel the shame of being sent to "the punishment corner" of the classroom by my teacher Mrs. Whistler. Her bright red fingernails pierced my neck, her words and frown shook and taunted me. *I may have to hold you back a grade,* she'd hissed. Behaving in class and doing schoolwork didn't come naturally to me; I'd spent so much time those days worrying about my mom that I had a really hard time focusing in school. All that early anxiety had curled itself into rock, which lived stubbornly in the pit of my stomach. I wanted to be a carefree kid, but I was struggling—depressed about my mom's health (always poor), my dad's moods (always angry), and generally buzzing at a low frequency. I felt like something was wrong with me, and Mrs. Whistler's sharp words and nails didn't help the cause. But deep in my belly, close to where that anxious rock sat around, was a flicker of hope and determination. Questions played ping-pong across my brain: *Can I take this* *unhappiness and turn it into something else? Can I learn from it, and use it somehow? Why can't I ever pay attention or do well in school? Is something *really* wrong with me, or does it just feel that way? And doesn't everyone feel that way sometimes, too?*

Fifth grade (I was not held back, thank you very much!) brought much welcomed change. This was the year I discovered reading. When I was reading, I felt less alone. My anxiety would disappear and instead I felt moments of clarity and confidence. Nothing was wrong with me after all! My first favorite book was *The Black Stallion* by Walter Farley. I read it in one gulp, hiding a light under the covers one night to finish. The next day I raced to the library to take home all of Farley's sequels, and many other books, too. Soon, I was having reading competitions with my friend to see who could read the most books per week. And at home—where family trouble always seemed to brew—I could retreat to my room, shut the door and focus my imagination on a better place. Reading saved me, and opened my mind to the richness of the world. The feeling was like putting on glasses for the first time; the world suddenly looks different. Trees are no longer green blobs; they have individual leaves. Distant mountains aren't grey; they have color and texture. It was an awakening. My confidence increased and my curiosity took off. By seventh grade, I'd overcome my problems at school, and I was at the top of my class. (Take that, Mrs. Whistler. But also, *thank you* Mrs. Whistler—for pushing me to persevere.)

By now you can see that I was off to a pretty slow start—and not just academically. Here's a secret: slow to start does not mean slow to finish. After all those early hurdles—and alas, many more to come—the adventure of my professional life has been fantastic, rewarding and prosperous. In my career, I developed and helped find cures for diseases such as cancer and HIV/AIDS. I created more than a dozen biotechnology companies and influenced public policy at the highest levels. I built two foundations, one to foster collaboration between the arts and science, and another—ACCESS Health International— to advise governments worldwide on how to bring high-quality, affordable healthcare to all. Along the way, I have had the privilege of forming lifelong friendships with world-renowned actors, artists, musicians, writers, economists, business titans, military men and women, and politicians. To boot, I have had a richly fulfilling personal and family life. In 2001, *TIME Magazine* named me one of the "25 Most Influential Global Business Executives" and in 2015, and *Scientific American* named me one of the 100 most influential leaders in biotechnology. It is a deep honor to be recognized in this way.

For me, science provided a way out of trouble and a path to opportunity. Science lets you be your own boss. It can give you independence at a very young age and since the field is so vast—science runs the gamut from research to rockets to ribosomes!— you can explore ideas based on your own interests and personal curiosities.

Before we really dig into the story of my lifelong fight against disease and the heroes who made it possible, the final point I'd like to leave you with is this: science cannot happen in a vacuum, nor can change. Science is dependent on teamwork. Heroes cannot act alone. This is why my story so heavily relies on the experiences and discoveries of others. As scientists and future-scientists, mentors and mentees, masters and students, we must all learn from one another. This being said, I hope you'll be inspired by my stories, moved to pursue a life in science and someday make your own contributions to improve human life. And when that happens, I'll be the one reading your stories.

Science is dependent on teamwork. Heroes cannot act alone.

***

(Just one more thing: a life of science tends to lead to a life of big words and big ideas. Words that make your mouth work overtime, like *aldehyde* and *polypectomy*. Many terms you'll be familiar with, and others I'll explain as I go. For all the words and phrases presented in **bold** text, however, you'll find those defined in the Glossary of Terms in the back of the book.)

Onward!

CHAPTER 1

Penicillin, Polio, And Microbes

If it weren't for a Scottish scientist named Alexander Fleming, I wouldn't be writing this book. In fact, if it weren't for Alexander Fleming, I wouldn't be alive! When I was just four months old, I fell very ill. Alexander Fleming had recently discovered the antibiotic, penicillin, but it was not yet widely available. Thankfully, I was one of the lucky few able to receive the breakthrough drug, and it saved my life.

Have you ever noticed when the bread stays too long on the counter, it starts to turn a little green, and sometimes white, and sometimes fuzzy? That's mold, and mold is *everywhere*. Sometimes it's on cheese, and you can even eat it. Sometimes it's in the shower, sometimes it's in the bushes, and sometimes you need a microscope to see it. Alexander Fleming was studying different bacteria in his lab, way back in the late 1920s, when he noticed that certain bacteria wouldn't grow when certain mold was nearby. This was an amazing and important discovery. From that mold (called *penicillium notatum*), Fleming was able to develop the antibacterial drug—penicillin—that could be used to treat infections and prevent harmful bacterium from growing out of control and making people sick. People called penicillin a miracle drug and I agree; without penicillin, my story would have ended before it began.

Of course, at only four months old, I was too young to actually *remember* receiving penicillin, but just knowing I did was later very meaningful to me. Surviving a close brush with death when I was a baby was a catalyst for my lifelong passion for using research, discovery, and scientific innovation to save lives.

Alexander Fleming and his accidental discovery that saved my life, penicillin.

What I *do* remember from my childhood was living with the threat and terror of polio, another serious infectious disease that could—and did—leave many young kids paralyzed. That constant threat of disease when I was young shaped my thoughts about illness, medicine, and science. One of the scariest (and strangest) things about polio was how close in relation it was to the common cold; it was like a cold virus gone bad, turned evil. Sound familiar? COVID-19 is similar; both are unfriendly cousins to viruses that cause the common cold. Polio struck suddenly, seemingly at random, during the summer months. The effects it could have on children in particular were horrible. Swimming, my favorite summertime relief from the heat, was now forbidden. So too were the cool dark theaters where I longed to see movies with my friends. And speaking of friends, we were only allowed to see just one or two at a time. Camp and recreation activities were off the table. We were told to stay at home and isolate; we waited impatiently for science to save us, for a vaccine to protect us or a drug we might need to cure us. I bet it's a lot like how you felt waiting for vaccines for COVID-19.

We waited impatiently for science to save us, for a vaccine to protect us or a drug we might need to cure us.

Eventually, the cavalry of scientists arrived led by Jonas Salk and Albert Sapin. After they discovered vaccines for polio, cases plummeted. Here are helpful figures for perspective: in 1952, the peak year of the U.S. polio outbreak, 58,000 cases were recorded. The Salk vaccine (injected with a syringe) was introduced in 1955, and following mass immunizations, cases plunged to just 161 by 1961. The Sabin vaccine (given orally) was introduced in the U.S. in 1962; the oral vaccine made it even easier for people to be vaccinated and it reduced the spread of disease significantly. The vaccines brought a collective sigh of relief—globally, of course, but also in my home. My parents, riddled as they were with tension and dysfunction, could suddenly breathe a bit easier, and my siblings and I could finally get back to the pool.

But let's back up for a moment. What exactly *is* a vaccine, and why do we need them to combat viruses and bacterial infections? What does a vaccine *do*? It's important to know that a vaccine is not a shield of armor; you can still sometimes become infected with a viral or bacterial **pathogen** even if you're vaccinated against it. But vaccines can prevent that pathogen from making you ill. Essentially, vaccines protect your immune system from being bullied into sickness. Fun/weird/important fact: vaccines are usually made from the very pathogens themselves. When *purposely* exposing your body to a weakened—or dead—disease pathogen, it causes your body to create antibodies to fight that disease. Then, if you're infected with the *live* pathogen, your body knows immediately what to do—it sends those antibodies straight after the invader. What is more, long-term immunity is created.

Vaccines, however, can't fight disease on their own. **Therapeutics** to cure disease once you are sick are important, too. Have you ever heard of something called an iron lung? Sounds like a superpower, right? It kind of is. Or at least it was during polio years. Technology has advanced quite a bit since these contraptions were in operation, so you won't see very many in hospitals these days, but they're important to know about, and crazy to look at! Since many polio patients had respiratory issues, they needed mechanical breathing assistance. These tank chambers were built to simulate breathing and save lives. Plus, they looked like little spaceships.

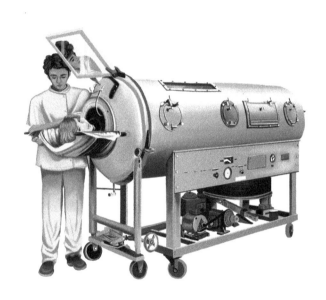

As you've experienced with COVID-19, and as I experienced with polio, when your early years are disrupted by widespread illness, the world can seem very scary. You may also feel powerless too—unable to steer the course of your own life, much less make a difference in the world around you. For me, looking to heroes like Alexander Fleming, Jonas Salk, and Albert Sabin helped me to understand that science can help anyone—even a very young person—improve their own life and make a positive difference in the lives of thousands, even millions, of those around them. When I realized this, I started asking my own questions and performing my own experiments.

***

Let me take you back in time to my seventh grade science fair. A little stage was set; a large jar containing a dozen preserved *Rana pipiens* (common leopard frogs) was at my elbow.

"The frog is very different from us on the outside but inside it looks like us," I explained to onlookers. Pointing with one hand and separating tissue in each frog with a small scalpel in the other, I would continue, "Here is the heart, lungs, liver, intestines, kidneys and spleen. All pretty much in the same place as ours." The adults were interested and the kids were fascinated. I was teaching something immediately relevant to them, the anatomy of their own bodies. "Look at the leg muscles. Feel your own. Don't they seem to be in the same place? Can you jump?" I stayed at my table all afternoon, until the jar was empty. That night I went to bed happy. Turned out, science wasn't cool to just me; it was applicable and interesting to all.

My very first independent experiments were a little more…awesome. It was time to play with explosives. I read up on the ingredients of gunpowder, then bought saltpeter and sulfur flour from the local pharmacy. These days, the cashier might raise an eyebrow or call a guard if you try to make such a purchase, but back then? No questions asked! I made my own charcoal, and ground ingredients in different ratios, looking for the perfect mix. It wasn't long before I was blowing up everything within reach.

My work bench was my bedroom desk. When a spark from a test mix ignited the main cache, my desk went up in flames instantly. Woops. Were it not for a handy fire extinguisher wielded by a very angry dad, the entire house might have gone up as well. After that, no more gunpowder.

But what about homemade rockets? My rocket of choice: an empty CO2 cylinder, like the type people use to make fizzy drinks. My fuel: matches, with shavings from the match heads ground to a fine powder. My launcher: a three foot long L shaped length of iron. The result: several holes punched though our one inch thick concrete garage wall. My reward: a month of weekend chores.

By the time I reached high school, I was still trying to figure out a lot about myself but one thing was certain: I loved freshman biology and the wild world of bacteria. "Is it true that these invisible organisms live *everywhere*?" I wondered. "Is it true that they cause disease? Is it true that to cure a bacterial infection you need to pair the right antibiotic to the right type of bacteria?" Of course, I had lived this experience when I was given penicillin as a baby, but now I had the tools to really ask questions.

Surviving a close brush with death when I was a baby was a catalyst for my lifelong passion for using research, discovery, and scientific innovation to save lives.

I swabbed every surface I could find—walls, tires, snake skin, bars of soap. To my delight each swab produced small mounds of bacteria, each appearing with different color and texture on plates I made in the kitchen by adding beef or chicken bouillon to agar (a jelly-like substance made from red seaweed). Yes, bacteria were everywhere—on doorknobs, windows, skin, lizards, tarantulas and even the soap! Under the microscope each had distinct shapes; rods, spheres, beads on a string and tightly connected hemispheres.

Were any bacteria dangerous? For the science fair in my sophomore year, my buddy and I planned a test of Koch's postulates (a system to check if a microorganism causes disease). We isolated bacteria from my throat, one yellow, one white. Then we injected the bacteria into rats. The rats injected with the yellow bacteria, but not the white bacteria, developed severe boils. Antibiotics that killed the yellow bacteria on our petri dishes cured the boils; those that had no effect in the petri dish had no effect on the rats either. Fascinating! Our winning project's name, "Bacteria: Dangerous or Not?"

Unfortunately, my part of the science project might have unleashed some potentially dangerous molecules in the bacteria. My dad came down with a high persistent fever. He was rushed to the hospital one afternoon with a temperature of 105 degrees. The bacteria I had stored in the family fridge were prime suspects. Woops again. My dad recovered—after ten days—but my home-brewed studies of bacteria were over for good.

CHAPTER 2

Parallax Vision and Seeing the World

If you've ever seen a fly up close, you know how outrageous their eyeballs are. A fly's eyes don't move the way ours do—in fact, they don't move at all. Instead, a fly's eyes are covered in *thousands* of visual receptors. Because a fly's eyes stick out from their head like two giant balloons, it gives them an almost 360-degree view of the world. Lucky fly.

For us humans, we struggle to see the world in the same way. Not only is our view of the world literally smaller because of the way our eyes work, our minds often narrow our perspective as well, making it hard to juggle multiple views about life. Especially growing up, it can be overwhelming to take in all the personalities and values swirling around you. It certainly was for me. Maybe you've felt the same? We have our parents, friends, enemies, teachers, siblings—the list goes on. And likely, all these people have different ideas about how the world works and where we fit in.

My parents had very different views about how a young boy should make his way in the world. My dad's approach was strict: honesty, hard work, self-discipline, play by the rules, merit wins the day. My mom, however, urged me and my siblings not to expect any favors in life, never to take no for answer. Be flexible and adapt. You will succeed or fail based only on your own efforts, she'd said. For me, trying to figure out whose path I should follow was challenging; I was forced to weigh two very different ideas about how to behave in life. I often wondered which world view to adopt, my father's or my mother's? They couldn't *both* be right, could they? Possibly, they are *both wrong*!

Though initially perplexing, this very act of questioning saved me from years of confusion, and set me on a path toward critical thinking. I questioned everything. And by questioning everything, I could learn from everything— my personal experience, my reading, my friends, my enemies, my teachers, my siblings and even my parents. *Then*: I could make up my own mind. By seeing the world with as-close-to-fly-eye as possible, taking in *all* the scientific wonder as well as all the art, music, culture, all the food, even all the weighty things like illness and war, I could form my own thoughts and ideas.

...questioning saved me from years of confusion, and set me on a path toward critical thinking. I questioned everything. And by questioning everything,

Once I became used to questioning everything, I came up with a new way to frame and solve problems, beyond asking questions alone. I call it my (get ready for another superpower…) *parallax vision*. The word "parallax" is an astronomy term; if you try to measure the distance to a faraway star, you will get a more accurate reading if you make your measurements from two different points on Earth, rather than just one. Astronomers call this method of measurement *stellar parallax* and I think it applies to just about everything. The more you look at things from different points of view, the better.

Parallax Vision (let's call it Super PV) helps you see things that others miss, and it can lead to new insights and adventures. When something seems impossible to question, or impossible to answer, that's when you turn your Super PV on. And don't forget to aim your Super PV at *yourself*, too, and look at your actions and decisions from different points of view. If—excuse me, *when*—you make your own important discoveries in life, I guarantee you'll need to employ this superpower. Examining different viewpoints will make you a more disciplined, confident explorer in whatever you choose to do. Later, when we dive deep into the paths I took in medical science and improving human health, you'll see just how powerful Super PV can be.

***

What's outside your window right now? Trees and grass? A stray cat? A subway station? An ocean? Maybe there's no window at all, or maybe it's closed. Is there a lamp on? A TV? And what's your neighborhood like? Is it full of people in their cars, rushing to work? Or is it pretty quiet? Are there mountains nearby? The environment that we live in—outside our homes and inside our homes, and across seas and borders, too—is so important. Our surroundings shape us, so we have to pay attention to them.

I grew up in a place called China Lake, California, at the western edge of the Mojave Desert. China Lake was a naval weapons research base, a small community where scientists designed and tested—mostly in secret!— new rockets, missiles and other weapons. My father was a physicist and many of my friends' parents were rocket scientists, engineers, jet pilots, and daredevil war aces. The father of one of my scouting buddies was William McLean, a Navy physicist who developed a heat-seeking short-range missile called the Sidewinder, named for the desert snake that can detect warm prey just by sensing its heat. I remember watching him putter with other inventions too, including an underwater bicycle. If you are an inventor, I learned, you apparently just cannot stop!

Watching these individuals work, I learned early on that one person, with the right energy, enthusiasm, and vision, can make a big difference in the world though science. But remember: Super PV asks us to look not *just* at science, not *just* at the cool rockets, but all around. China Lake was located in a valley surrounded by mountains and volcanic mounds. That landscape was formed four million years ago by clashing tectonic plates. Many eastern California fault lines ran below China Lake, attracting famous earthquake scientists, known as seismologists, for research.

I learned early on that one person, with the right energy, enthusiasm, and vision, can make a big difference in the world though science.

One day, when I was sixteen, I got an amazing lesson in how to measure the intensity of earthquakes as soon as they happen. If you know an earthquake's intensity, you can quickly guess how much damage it may have caused, near and far. A world-famous seismologist was sitting across from me when suddenly we felt the room shaking. He started tapping rhythmically with his forefinger, with a small, satisfying smile that grew wider and wider as he kept his eyes peeled to the second hand of his wristwatch.

(This was around 1960, long before digital watches were invented.) When the shaking stopped, I asked him what he had been doing. "Timing the intervals between the rolling surface wave and the vertical shocks," he replied, happily. Then, the lesson: "The first shock to hit is surface waves. The vertical shocks follow after they bounce off the core beneath the earth's mantle. The time lag tells your distance from the epicenter of the quake. That one was a small one because the epicenter is no more than a mile from here."

China Lake was not so fortunate a few years ago. Two big quakes struck over the Fourth of July holiday that were felt more than one hundred fifty miles away in Los Angeles. Damage to the naval base cost more than two billion dollars to repair. Fortunately, no one on the base or in neighboring towns was hurt badly.

The part of California I grew up in was ideal for hiking, with many beautiful views and different types of plants and animals. I used to wander into the desert and up into the mountains, nervous about rattlesnakes, sure, but always eager to explore. Closing my eyes now, I can see dark bushes in the light sand, a multicolored carpet of desert blooms after a spring rain. I see brilliant sunrises and sunsets, the white mountains turning to pink then purple under an evening sky above the shadow of the mountains. Rolls of clouds pile high atop the Sierra Nevada, dropping rain to the west, then sailing high and dry across our valley.

My parents—despite their many differences—did agree on one important thing: their love for knowledge, in any subject. In addition to valuing science, they shared a fascination with art, history, theatre, literature and classical music. My instrument in those days—not by choice mind you—was the giant, cumbersome *sousaphone*. Have you ever heard of such a thing!? I played in marching band throughout middle school and was too small to carry the fifty pound instrument, so they made a cart to hold the instrument upright. As I marched and played, someone else pulled the cart!

Despite the sousaphone ridiculousness, I was ultimately grateful for the efforts my parents made to expose my siblings and I to the arts and humanities. As a result, I became interested in science not just for the sake of science, but also for what science could contribute to human progress. I understood a bit more about the flow of human history, of culture, anthropology and art, and it helped me figure out how I fit into that moving stream. My parents' love for the humanities in a military community largely dedicated to scientific discovery was an important influence in forming and exercising my Super PV.

***

Once I began chipping away at *how* to see the world, I wanted to *actually do it*. In my last three years of high school, I was given the chance to do something really special—travel! The first summer I went to Japan; the next summer to New York City; and in my last year of high school, I traveled to Europe. It was the perfect time to travel; I was young enough to get swept up in the adventure but old enough to really pay attention to everything new I discovered. I also felt like I was finally starting to know myself—and that seemed like perfect timing too.

Traveling to Japan was an exotic adventure. It opened my mind to different cultures and subcultures, to unfamiliar ideas that changed my thinking. I began to see what that modern world was really like, not through books and stories but from personal experience. Or, as a scientist would put it: through direct observation. There was never a dull moment. I arrived in Japan on a 750-foot U.S. Navy transport ship. I visited Buddhist temples, climbed to the top of the 1,092-foot Tokyo Tower and admired the beauty of gardens, shrines, and emerald green rice patties. It wasn't all joyful, though. At the time, Japan was just beginning to recover from a devastating war; large sections of Tokyo had been flattened by American bombing raids in the 1940s, economies were struggling, and many families were still trying to get their lives back in order. This was difficult to see, but in looking at the realities of war, I made my Super PV even more powerful—I could see things now from the other side and it gave me new ways to think about the world.

The summer after my trip to Japan, I went on an adventure with a group of students in the opposite direction to visit the United Nations in New York City. We traveled across the country by bus and I remember looking out of the windows and imagining myself traveling through a dense jungle. All green on every side! I was so used to my desert life, that I found the endless green farmlands and hills fascinating. When we arrived in New York, the so-called Big Apple, my first impressions were not great. Buildings covered with grime. Dirty streets. Overcrowded sidewalks. But those thoughts faded quickly once we entered the U.N. headquarters, overlooking the East River. There, we met with important ambassadors and took part in mock debates on the hot topics of the day—equality, racism, and affordable healthcare. (Alas, you are probably very familiar with these issues too, as they still pose major challenges to our nation and beyond.)

I'd been on the debate team, and when your goal in life is to have an impact in health for the population of…well, the entire world…you have a responsibility to learn how to speak up. Debate team was a great confidence builder for me when I was young and it helped me in all of my jobs when I was older—medical sciences professor, antiwar activist, science funding advocate, and leader in research laboratories, businesses and nonprofit organizations. In debate, we would argue both sides of a question and we had to be prepared for presentation, counter presentation and cross examination. We learned to stand up and make an argument supported by fact, and to understand other people's arguments. We worked on impromptu speaking as well. Many years later I told our coach, Ann Cierley, how valuable her debate training had been throughout my entire life.

The last adventure I took during those years was to Europe, right after finishing high school. I was part of a group organized by American Youth Hostels; our plan was to bicycle for six weeks together, travel four weeks solo, and then all regroup for the trip home. I took the train from California and connected with my fellow travelers in New York. No visit to the shiny U.N. this time around; I had an international ocean liner to get to! We set sail to Europe on the Aurelia, a small slow Italian liner (side note: ships were a mighty good place to party those days, and nobody ever seemed to get tired). Our first overnight stop was in Bath, a city in England. We had traveled all the way from Southampton through Salisbury by bicycle before our eyes fixed on Bath's monstrous Bathwick Hill, which we had to climb while carrying all our gear. Once over the hill, we staggered to our resting stop for the night, a ninth century mill with a sagging roof and a working waterwheel. Oof, but also: *wow*. Cycling to London took us across a hundred miles of windy rolling backroads. After crossing the channel by boat, we cycled from Rotterdam north to Amsterdam, then south to Belgium and northern France. Naturally, we wanted to explore the west and south of France, too, Normandy to Brittany, more countryside magic before reaching Paris.

Pro tip: if you really want to see the countryside, travel by bicycle! The countryside rolls by gently no matter how hard you pedal and there's nothing like it. We passed fields filled with fruits we would be eating that evening. We'd reach the top of a hill and see cathedrals rising in the distance then disappear as we sped down the other side. After Paris, I was on my own; I headed south on my bicycle more than four hundred miles—thank you, knees and calves!— to the Spanish border, eastward and finally downward to Marseille, all stops full of fascinating history and *the best food ever*.

Similar to what I'd seen in Japan, however, much of Europe was still recovering from war. The northern cities, including Paris and London, were dark with soot. There was damage in East London and Rotterdam. Highways connecting major cities were still only two lanes wide. But this contrast was crucial for me to see. The marvelous and the not-so-marvelous. The beauty and the brutality. The light and the dark. They cannot exist without one another. To really hone our Super PV, and to really make a difference in this world, we have to understand both sides.

Foreign travel opens your mind. These three summer trips helped me form a purpose that would propel me further across the next decade of my life: I wanted to have a *global* impact and improve all human life, if I could. Those trips helped me appreciate the equal value of human life everywhere. We are all connected and we have to do our best to help everybody.

And about being connected—here's a super-important difference between my adolescence and yours: the internet. While experience abroad is often the fullest way to learn about other cultures, these days your mind can be opened nearly as wide by the wonderful world of online research. Sight-seeing bloggers abound with their first-hand accounts! Travel is not always an option for everyone, and it certainly isn't the only way to expand horizons. Curiosity, imagination and inquisitiveness are, however, *always* available, and with YouTube videos, Google Earth, and hundreds of millions of travel websites at our fingertips, we can go just about anywhere, anytime. I encourage you to strap on your parallax goggles and go see the world. Every inch of it. And when you're done with the world? Outer space.

Those trips helped me appreciate the equal value of human life everywhere. We are all connected and we have to do our best to help everybody.

***

Before chugging along to the What-Came-Next-For-Me, I want to take a moment to showcase some meaningful people in my life, my siblings: Florence, Eric, and Susan. There must have been something in our family experience and the China Lake environment that set us up for amazing success in science.

My older sister Florence has had a spectacular career. After graduating with honors in biophysics from University of California at Berkeley, she became one of the first women to receive a PhD in molecular biology at MIT (Massachusetts Institute of Technology). She built on that strong foundation, earning a medical degree from the Albert Einstein School of Medicine, then rising to chief resident in **obstetrics and gynecology** at Harvard's Boston Lying-in Hospital. Later, on the Yale Medical School faculty, she trained a generation of doctors in techniques of **in vitro fertilization**, then transitioned to government, leading funding for the National Institute of Child Health and Human Development at the National Institutes of Health. She directed that federal agency's Center for Population Research for nearly thirty years, introducing a policy to include women in clinical trials. She was founding editor of the *Journal for Women's Health*, and later founded the Society for the Advancement of

Women's Health Research. She is also an inventor with several inventions to her name, including one that improves how wheelchairs move.

And that's not all! She coauthored a book, *Woman Doctor*—a journey into gender bias against women in the medical professions in the 1960s and 1970s. It was a gutsy move, for any female physician to publish back then and given the content, the book could have really hurt her career. But she did it anyways. Go, Florence! Or maybe I should say, *Stay*, Florence, because as it turns out she's not going anywhere. Not even if she tried. Florence tried to retire in her early seventies, but it ended up to be just a pause. In 2019, at age seventy-six, she became a distinguished professor with tenure, teaching graduate nursing courses at the University of Texas at Arlington. The takeaway? We should plan for at least three or four careers in our lifetimes, into our eighties.

My younger brother Eric also has had a wonderful career. After studying economics and psychology at UC Berkeley, he received a PhD in neuroscience at Indiana University, then became a manager and engineering director at Hughes Aircraft, creating flight simulators to train fighter pilots. A cool gig, but it gets even cooler. My brother also worked at Walt Disney Imagineering—the research and development branch of Mickey's empire in charge of designing and creating Disney parks and attractions worldwide. Eric created large virtual reality experiences at the parks. In time he was promoted to chief technical officer of the entire corporation, responsible for all the technical aspects of Disney ventures including theme parks and the ABC television network. Following the awful 9/11 attacks in 2001, the government recruited Eric to become head of research at the National Security Agency. He later led the technical side of *all* our nation's intelligence services in the Office of the Director of National Intelligence. Eric still consults with our intelligence services and for Disney too, designing augmented reality toys such as headset-display storytelling devices. He is the author of a growing list of books on topics as diverse as his interests. And if that's not enough, he also chairs the U.S. Technology Leadership Council, which gives industry leaders, government officials, and university researchers the opportunity to meet and exchange ideas about science and technology.

Our sister Susan, also brilliant, has chosen a much quieter life. Quiet brilliance—that's a superpower, too.

CHAPTER 3

Masters, Mars, And Lasers

"We are sory..."

It was springtime, my senior year of high school. My classmates and I were eager to clean out our lockers, graduate, and move up and out. In April, I received one envelope and one postcard in the mail. The envelope was from my first choice for my university studies: Harvard. It was a rejection, with the above typo as the very first sentence. I was disappointed but trusted there'd be alternative paths. And I thought to myself, at least they're sory!

The postcard was from UC Berkeley, where my older sister was finishing her sophomore year. On the back were two small boxes beside the words: "Accepted" and "Not Accepted." The box next to "Accepted" was checked. How simple and clear they'd made it! I was disappointed about Harvard, but looking back, that rejection letter was a lucky twist of fortune. Berkeley in 1962 turned out to be an ideal place for me. Anybody with a B average in a California high school was accepted and the student body was socially, ethnically and culturally diverse. But perhaps the best part was that the students made their own choices on how to approach each day—there were no rules dictating when or how we had to do our work.

I was disappointed about Harvard, but looking back, that rejection letter was a lucky twist of fortune.

More than one hundred Nobel prize winners studied at UC Berkeley, including a few dozen Pulitzer Prize recipients, Academy Award winners, many members of Congress and about forty billionaires. Not a bad track record, I'd say.

The Berkeley campus was a wonderful place to broaden your mind, to have new experiences and to meet and learn from people with different viewpoints. I started as a pre-med major, taking all the courses I'd need to get into medical school—math, chemistry, physics and biology for the first two years— along with other courses like political science, history, literature and a foreign language, French, in my case. Even UC Berkeley seemed to understand the power of Super PV and the school became an excellent place to flex my PV muscles.

This new environment—and my newfound freedom— was beyond exciting. But I still had doubts. Could I really make it here? Could I achieve the goals I set for myself? Questions were springing up like weeds in my mind as I sat in my freshman dorm room which was furnished with the basics: bunkbed, desk, chair, and too-bright lamp. Freedom, I've learned, often comes with uncertainty. And in the case of freshman year at college, that uncertainty is just one notch away from downright fear. I was scared and anxious, sitting there at the brink of so much excitement and information. I knew I had to channel that anxiety, not waste the opportunity, and turn it into toward something positive.

My solution to anxiety was to plan, organize, and prepare; repeat, take a sip of water, and repeat again. I'd used a version of this approach during my summer travels in Europe, to make sense of everything that was so new and different. And Berkeley was definition that: a sprawling campus, with multilayered cultures and subcultures of faculty, students, administration; the immediate Berkeley community, gritty working class Oakland to the south and alluring San Francisco across the Bay Bridge. So, the planning commenced: find a place to live, then set a routine. I scheduled all my classes to start at 8:00 a.m. and finish by 1:00 p.m. The afternoon and early evening were for studying, with a break for dinner then back to the books. I would be in bed by 9:30 p.m., wake at 6:30 a.m., sometimes earlier. I know, I know, college is also for having fun—and I did, I swear!—but if I hadn't established this strict regimen early on, I may have lost myself. It's good to know yourself in this way. When you're afraid or anxious, do what *you* need to do to succeed.

I knew I had to channel that anxiety, not waste the opportunity, and turn it into toward something positive.

After lunch, it was right back to my dorm room to analyze my notes from morning classes. This habit of immediately reviewing everything I learned gave me a deeper understanding of what I was learning. It also gave me opportunities to ask my professors about anything I didn't understand. I rewrote all of my notes, incorporating details from references I had looked up. I then asked myself, what key issues would the professor likely ask us on quizzes or exams? Then, I wrote out essay answers so specific they noted and summarized references, including some I discovered in my own reading. This rigorous approach, unusual as it was among many of my peers, always paid off. I still got nervous and uneasy when exams rolled around, but I needed to be confident. Otherwise, all my steadfast hunkering would have been in vain, right? My first semester grades were all As. For this anxious teenager from China Lake, it was a *huge* relief. A thought crossed my mind: "Okay, I can relax," but I quickly barricaded that notion. "Not too much…I am going to keep my focus."

If you asked me for some big sweeping wisdom about college—and well, life in general—here's what I'd say: Persistence and determination *matter*. Strength of will *matters*. Developing confidence matters. Knowing your purpose matters and if you don't know your purpose yet, the journey to finding it can be incredibly fun too. Learn to tap into your strength of will. Whenever some obstacle is in your way, even if that obstacle is massive, you can silence any doubts in your mind that you are going to work through the problem and get past it. You just keep going until you do.

Developing confidence matters. Knowing your purpose matters and if you don't know your purpose yet, the journey to finding it can be incredibly fun too.

***

Remember how I said I thought I'd become a doctor? That's why at first I was a pre-med major at Berkeley. But I changed my mind about taking that particular path. Before the end of my freshman year, a brilliant educator and scientist selected me and a handful of others for a special program that would lead me from medicine toward science.

Following first semester chemistry, pre-med students were required to take a lab class to complement our work. Fine by me; maybe I'd get the chance to start small explosions again! I was enthusiastic about the experiments, curious at each turn. And I suppose it showed. One day that winter, a very senior professor came over and said to me, casually, "You know, Dr. Pimentel would like you to stop by his office." Dr. Pimentel was chair of the chemistry department. *Me?*, I thought, *why does he want to see me?*

The day I walked into his office, George C. Pimentel had been at Berkeley for fifteen years, including his PhD studies. During this time, he'd invented tools for analyzing molecules through **spectroscopy**—a huge advance in identifying, preventing and curing disease. He'd coauthored books on modern chemistry, and he'd directed a national program to rewrite high school chemistry teaching materials, emphasizing experiments and observation over abstract theory. He taught freshman chemistry class to thousands of students with enthusiasm—eyes wide, standing at the front of the class, and arms moving all about.

Raised in poverty by his mother and his construction-worker father during the Great Depression, Pimentel didn't let his trying background stop him from working his way through university to earn a diploma in physical chemistry. He moved to the Berkeley campus for his first job, a secret government project, where he examined chemical processes in the separation of **plutonium**. He also had a passion for space exploration; he nearly became a scientist-astronaut for NASA, if only he hadn't failed the vision test!. But he did lead the design of an **infrared spectrometer** to study Mars's atmosphere. To say his work was (literally) out of this world would be an understatement.

Pimentel reminds me of an important nugget from the previous chapter: a slow start does not mean slow to finish. Pimentel's path from poverty to success is not only inspiring, it's also roof that anyone from anywhere can harness the power of science. George C. Pimentel was a great mentor to me—and to many others as well. He was a beloved educator and an endlessly innovative scientist.

A slow start does not mean slow to finish.

So, you can see why I was so stunned to be in his office that day, sitting across from this superstar of science. That year, Pimentel had asked senior faculty members to keep an eye out for promising students. He vetted the nominees as possible candidates for a summer retreat with a group of top scientists. I was one of a dozen students in 1962 that he and his field marshals fished out of that freshman chemistry pool of three thousand students.

"I am looking for people who could work here in a summer program," he said. "We pay enough for room and board...I think you might like it."

"Sure!," I blurted out excitedly.

Before I knew it, I was part of something incredible. Pimentel's idea for the students that summer was simple: Nurture an excitement for science. Start them thinking about a life in science, and what that could look like. For six weeks, in this small group, we reviewed, studied, and met one great scientist per week. This was the stellar lineup Pimentel assembled:

- Melvin Calvin, whose name you might recognize from your textbooks. Known for his discoveries in **photosynthesis** and the eponymous **Calvin cycle,** this outstanding biochemist won the Nobel Prize in 1961.

- Harold Urey, another Nobel Prize winner, whose work revolved around **isotopes** and something called "heavy water"—water with an extra hydrogen neutron.

- Owen Chamberlain, *another* Nobel Prize winner, who discovered the **antiproton**; experiments with antiprotons have added clues for solving the mystery of the origins of the universe, the **Big Bang**.

- Luis Alvarez, who observed in the late 1950s how molecules fall apart when bombarded in a **hydrogen bubble chamber**—a pivotal finding for understanding the fundamental structure of the universe. (Oh, also...he won the Nobel Prize!)

- Joel Hildebrand, adored professor to over forty thousand freshman chemistry students at Berkeley. (I had practically memorized for that course his classic textbook, *Principles of Chemistry*.)

Talking with these brilliant masters was thrilling—like shooting hoops with LeBron James or Steph Curry, or singing scales with a group of world-renowned composers. I felt lucky and was eager to absorb everything I could. Listening to these masters, learning how they came to ask the questions they did and design experiments to answer them was life-changing. I remember Melvin Calvin saying to me—casually and as if his words weren't as exciting as they were—"Maybe you would want to work in my lab one day." It was the capstone to an electrifying year of opening my mind to new possibilities about science. Awestruck as I was, though, I came to realize that at some level these heroic figures were human, too, with distinct personalities and temperaments. Yes, they have super brains. Yes, they have made a huge impact. But their Olympian achievements now seemed more vivid, more accessible.

A spark flared in my teenage brain. If they once were just guys like me, maybe…

***

Who here wants to return to the topic of outer space, specifically Mars? Me too; let's do it.

As I mentioned, one of Pimentel's massive contributions to science was the infrared spectrometer that could detect and analyze gases and other elements in Mars's atmosphere. With his encyclopedic understanding of infrared spectrometer chemistry, Pimentel was one of the scientists racing to answer the question: Is there life on Mars? A scientist named Sinton noticed patterns in the Martian atmosphere and published data suggesting **aldehydes** might be the cause, and that those aldehydes may be a sign of life on Mars. That was big news. Aliens! (Well, maybe not *alien-aliens* but at least some sort of alien fungus or microorganism.) Pimentel questioned Sinton's interpretation, though; Earth has many life forms—trees, bugs, me, you—but there's very little aldehyde in our atmosphere. So, how could they exist on Mars?

"Bill," Pimentel said, "you're going to help me find the answers." At this point, I was back for my second summer program. I paired up with a talented graduate student and together we designed and conducted experiments. If aldehydes *did* exist in Mars's atmosphere, we believed the amount likely was very small because aldehyde molecules did not stay stable for long before decomposing. Harold Urey's "heavy water", however, absorbed infrared similar to that of aldehydes. Had Sinton goofed and mistaken heavy water for aldehydes? After creating a series of model atmospheres, measuring the light that passed through each one, we eventually reproduced the pattern Sinton had observed. After interpreting the data, we concluded that yes!— he'd detected evidence for heavy water in Mars's atmosphere, *not* aldehydes. His conclusion—the leading scientific argument for life on Mars—was incorrect.

"We need to publish these results as soon as possible," George Pimentel said. "Bill, you conducted the experiments. You take the lead in writing. We'll submit it first to *Science*." This set my pulse racing. *Science* was— and still is—one of the most influential science publications. Getting published is extremely competitive, highly prized by even the most accomplished scientists. Only ten papers are published in each issue. My very first published scientific paper… in *Science*! "Here," I thought, "is *my* contribution to human knowledge on a major question: Is there life on Mars?" I felt extremely proud—confident with the work we'd done, but still in a bit of disbelief that I was a part of this high-level scientific conversation.

That was not the end of the Sinton story, however. When I was a senior, a couple years later, another Mars-related paper appeared in *Science*. The authors concluded that the heavy water was not in Mars's atmosphere, after all. It was in *Earth's* atmosphere. Why? When Sinton measured Earth's atmosphere by pointing his telescope at the moon, the humidity was very low. On the days he observed Mars (during its closest approach to Earth) the humidity was high. We had not considered that key point.

This story exhibited a fundamental and humbling truth about the scientific method. I suggest keeping this one in your back pocket, as it's been in mine for years: science does not reveal truth. Rather, science provides tools for testing ideas, hypotheses. Your measurements may be correct, but your *interpretations* may be wrong. But wrong is good sometimes; wrong helps answer questions.

...science does not reveal truth. Rather, science provides tools for testing ideas, hypotheses.

Other questions Pimentel gave us that second summer: What might life be like on another planet? In another galaxy? In another universe? In other words, what distinguishes life from other forms of matter and energy? This is a question that has fascinated philosophers for ages but it had a real use—if NASA were to design instruments to detect life in our universe, what were they looking for? We met each week to discuss our thoughts; the discussions were lively, led by Pimentel in **Socratic dialogue**. He never said, "This is what I think." He always asked, "What do you think?"

Which reminds me: What do *you* think?

I came up with this simple(ish) formulation that I continue to hold today: A living system is one that is capable of reproducing itself, with errors. The errors allow a system that keeps remaking itself (what's known as a self-replicating system) to adapt to its environment. This description of living systems is independent of substance. Life on Earth is based on carbon. As American astronomer, cosmologist, and astrophysicist Carl Sagan once staid: *we are made of star stuff*. Literally! Other living systems may be based on other elements such as silicon or even on energy alone. I have never stopped thinking about the nature and origin of life.

In time I added one more condition to my definition: sustained **energy input**. One of the fundamental observations of our world is that energy gets used up, right? It doesn't stand still or sit on the couch; it's in constant motion, flowing from one thing to the next. Without a source of additional energy, order becomes disorder. Life on Earth exists in a thin energy rich shell. The crust of our planet is continually enriched by the flow of massive amounts of energy—radiation energy from the sun above and intense heat from our molten core below. If we *do* discover other living systems on a distant planet we will only find them in energy rich environments. (Apologies if anyone is starting to crave molten chocolate lava cake with a graham cracker crust; sometimes this happens when I start talking about our planet.)

***

That second year of summer duty in George Pimentel's lab was an extraordinary gift. I was on the frontlines of science, trying to answer some of the biggest questions of the day. It would have been fantastic to be known as the Berkeley undergrad who found proof of life on Mars. But disproving Sinton's hypothesis and then having my own results disproved was still deeply satisfying, because it gave me a first-hand lesson in *the process* of science—

questioning, testing, interpreting, then questioning all over again. Sometimes your own interpretations are overturned, and that's okay. Talking with and studying the lives of great scientists at Berkeley showed me how scientific knowledge is passed from generation to generation. Somebody makes a discovery. Then, people fight about it: Is it true? Is it not true? They come to a consensus: this most likely is true. That consensus enters the textbooks because everyone agreed something was probably true, not necessarily because it *is* true. The contents of your science textbooks are the result of generations of scientists working together to find the most likely answer to a particular question, then that fundamental research is explained by the authors of the book as they understood it at the time. But people *continue* to create knowledge. Just like energy, knowledge is always moving, never static. And, remember, knowledge is power. A fantastic superpower!

The contents of your science textbooks are the result of generations of scientists working together to find the most likely answer to a particular question, then that fundamental research is explained by the authors of the book as they understood it at the time.

It seemed, I, too, was always moving. The following summer, after my junior year—time flies when you're on

Mars!—I'd head to another lab, this time way on the other side of the country at MIT (Massachusetts Institute of Technology). But shortly before heading east, I had my first experience with what would become my passion: molecular biology. I was working with a Berkeley chemist, Ignacio Tinocco, who was interested in the fundamental properties of **DNA and RNA.**

"I am working on a theory that would enable us to predict the shape form sequence," Tinocco explained to me. "You'll help me with the experiments." To accomplish this goal, we needed to understand the fundamental properties of each of the units called **nucleosides**, the basic building blocks of DNA and RNA. "Your job," he continued, "will be to determine the solubility of each of the units in a solution that mimics the interior of a cell."

Okay, so what in the world does this all mean, and what was I supposed to do? Solubility is the ability of a substance (the solute), to mix into a liquid (the solvent). So, for this experiment, I had to seal small amounts of each compound in a mild salt solution, then rock them gently (no lullaby required) in a warm body-temperature bath for several weeks. I then measured the amount of light absorbed by the liquid. That allowed me to determine the concentration, and therefore the solubility of each unit. These numbers, the results of my third year Berkeley biochemistry project, are still cited in fundamental chemistry textbooks. Not only did this experiment ignite my interest in molecular biology, but it also prepared me for the DNA-related work I'd do at the MIT lab soon after.

***

By now you know how fond I am of space, lasers, and minor explosions. For many, these things are only experienced in the movies or science-fiction novels. But if you pursue a path of science—all three are right there at your fingertips.

For my senior thesis, I returned to space. The great beyond. The big starry soup. "We need to learn more about sending messages from Earth into space with lasers," George Pimentel told me. "Brad Moore can help you get started." Moore was an assistant professor and one of the first chemists to use lasers. Working with Pimentel, he made important discoveries on energy transfer in molecules, the kinetics of chemical reactions and **photochemistry**—all imperative to our understanding of atmospheric and **combustion chemistry**.

"We want a clearer understanding of vibrations between linked atoms," Brad said, framing my role. This was

NASA-funded research project that would help make voice communications between ground control and astronauts in the command module clearer and more reliable. The clock was ticking on President John F. Kennedy's goal to get American astronauts safely to the moon and back before the end of 1969. "We need to look at how light is emitted and absorbed by molecules," Brad explained.

The light emitted by the types of lasers used at that time could be absorbed by Earth's atmospheric carbon dioxide. This was a problem for space communications; messages communicated with these lasers could not be transmitted from ground control through our atmosphere to astronauts anywhere above the atmosphere. I thought about what I'd previously learned about heavy water. Might light emitted by a carbon dioxide laser with a heavier isotope replacing normal oxygen solve the problem?

"Heavier oxygen slows the speed of vibration," I confirmed with Brad. "If we substitute heavier oxygen for normal oxygen, could that change the character of the light so that it could pass through our atmosphere without losing intensity?"

"Good idea," he said, and we set about designing experiments to test my hypothesis.

Throughout that semester, I worked on building more and more powerful lasers. Eventually, it worked! My hypothesis was correct. To demonstrate this, I sent light beams from Latimer Hall on the Berkeley campus more than seven miles across the bay to San Francisco that were *so* powerful they could drill a hole through a brick wall. This was astonishing and FUN. And it proved that certain lasers were more than capable of carrying messages beyond our atmosphere. My paper on these findings was published in the journal *Applied Physics Letters*.

***

Beyond science, I also studied the humanities—all the other things that make humans tick, like history, literature, art and philosophy. I picked cultural anthropology as a minor, and also studied political science, western intellectual history and several history courses on China, Japan and South America. In this well-rounded environment, I became convinced more deeply than before that science must address critical *human needs*. Science can take you very thoroughly into any subject. Science can answer extremely important questions, big questions. But to know which questions to ask, you need that big-picture understanding of human history, the arts, physical and cultural anthropology, philosophy and literature. You need to know where society has been and where it may be going. Science is a human endeavor. To know which questions to ask, it helps to know why different tribes and cultures emerged, triumphed, wavered and collapsed. What technologies did they use? What values did they hold? What rituals and traditions? What diseases did they suffer from? Asking these questions, I realized—and I'm sure you have, too—that life can be difficult. It may be brutal, harsh. This is the nature of human existence, and probably the existence of all living things.

Science can answer extremely important questions, big questions. But to know which questions to ask, you need that big-picture understanding of human history, the arts, physical and cultural anthropology, philosophy and literature.

Yet, after all the conflict is burned away by time, what is left is beauty—great beauty, great intellectual achievements. This is a completely different part of humanity, one that we can celebrate. And…our accumulated knowledge remains. Our mathematics. Our language. Our music. Our art. Our science. Our technologies. So we can *enjoy* this great beauty. It is part of what can keep you very happy, with the capacity to enjoy every moment.

My hard work and discipline at school paid off with more A grades and the attention of outstanding professors. I discovered from long hours in laboratories, meeting scientists, and asking All Those Very Big Questions that I truly *loved* science. Couldn't live without it. I should also mention here all the *fun* I had at university outside the lab—the college parties I planned, the friends I made— our parallax vision deserves to attend a house party or concert or ice cream shop every once in a while! By the end of my time at Berkeley I actually believed that I mighte be able to achieve my childhood goal—to improve human health. I couldn't wait for what would come next.

CHAPTER 4

Activism, Genes, And Late-Night Labs

As you read my story, I hope you keep in mind your own story as well. A lot of my experience probably echoes your own, especially what you've been experiencing in recent years since the start of COVID. In the summer of 2020, when a lot of business had shut down and schools had closed, there was swell of political activism. A lot of it was tied to what people were watching at home on the news—police brutality and the unequal treatment of different groups of Americans. People marched in the streets to voice their dissent, and that's similar to what was going on when I was in college as well. We were out on the streets too, fighting for free speech, equal rights and protesting America's role in the **Vietnam War.**

Having grown up in China Lake—surrounded by weapons— I knew the devastating effect war and weapons could have on people's lives. Knowing this, I started joining campus protests and rallies. Listening to speakers during one of the Berkeley antiwar rallies, I thought: *These people have a point. Why are we fighting this war?* As a science-minded student, always looking for data and reason, it seemed to me that there was no reason for this war. I also couldn't find a reason for why we treated people differently just because of where they were born or the color of their skin, and I suspect you cannot either.

When I arrived in Cambridge, Massachusetts for my internship at the MIT lab, the antiwar movement was spreading to campuses all over the country. Not only students but many professors at Harvard and MIT, including mine, were also involved. I was inspired by them and eager to participate. Then—and later when I was at graduate school—I questioned the particular role of science and scientists in waging or preventing war as part of a scientist's duty to society. Many of the scientists I respected spoke out about how science should be used responsibly. As a result, I began to think much harder about how wealth is distributed in American society, and America's unequal social conditions. I needed to understand the implications of America's war in Vietnam, and to decide how I should respond *as a scientist*.

I came to believe, and still do, that every society supports science in the hopes that science will eventually lead to benefits for society. My interest in using science to improve human health only deepened in this antiwar era. These experiences would, in the next decade, help fuel my desire to take up arms through the science I came to know best—molecular biology—in the fight against disease.

Every society supports science in the hopes that science will eventually lead to benefits for society. My interest in using science to improve human health only deepened in this antiwar era.

***

The summer of 1966—in between my Berkeley graduation and my first semester at graduate school (Harvard, ahem, "sory" no more!)—I used my savings to to travel again, from Japan to England, through the Indus Valley and Fertile Crescent. I thought: *I've been devoted to my schoolwork for four years now, and at this rate, it looks like things will continue in this manner well...forever.* So what did I need? A vacation.

This trip across northern India, by train, bus and an occasional rickshaw or hired car, after flying into Calcutta from Thailand, would be the defining experience of my three month trip, and one of the most significant of my life. And as I quickly learned, "a vacation" doesn't always include beach parties and exotic snacks. Quite the opposite, in this case. When I first stepped outside my hotel in the center of Calcutta, I was shocked. Dead and dying people filled the streets. Workers were loading lifeless bodies onto carts to be taken who-knows-where. I saw people with leprosy—people with no hands, no eyes, no nose. People whose bodies were horribly twisted. These terrible scenes haunted me, images I still carry in my memories. "I am going to do whatever I can to help sick people," I kept repeating to myself on those long travels—and have never stopped.

That summer included adventures I never could have planned. There was even a narrow escape from military chaos that might have trapped me in one country, Syria, for who-knows-how long. Months, probably. Mostly, though, the trip was fun. I saw fabulous jewels, historic ruins of the Roman Empire, the Great Pyramids in Egypt, and made many new friends.

I am going to do whatever I can to help sick people...

When I arrived at Harvard that September, I was extremely grateful (x10) for my one bedroom apartment. Here I had running water. I had a shower and a toilet that worked. The heating worked. The plumbing worked. People were not starving all around me. I realized that we are extremely privileged. I have felt deeply grateful ever since for being lucky enough to live comfortably and to do the work I love. Each morning, in a short meditation sandwiched in between brushing my teeth and combing my hair, I remembered my good fortune and looked forward to the day.

***

You've heard me mention *molecular biology* a few times now. Let's go deeper into what that is exactly, and how/why/when it became my preferred field of study. Molecular biology—closely related to biochemistry— focuses on the interactions between cell systems, including DNA, RNA and **protein synthesis** and learning how these interactions work. At Harvard, I was determined to study the sciences as deeply as possible; I wanted to master advanced theoretical physics, chemistry and applied mathematics. Much to do, much to learn. Completing these courses would help me explore a *wide* range of scientific questions related to health, whether I became a physician or medical scientist. I did not want to be limited by a lack of knowledge in any of these fields. Many of these advanced science classes this first year were taught by Nobel laureates or future Nobel laureates. Despite my previous exposure to and experience with great minds, it still dazzled me to be among these heroes.

Structural biology was my favorite course. The class introduced me to the logic and beauty of biological structures. Here I was again, being presented with the confluence of art and science. Ever since, whenever I look at the leaves of a tree or the shape of a sea shell, I marvel at the function and beauty of their form. Mother Nature invented form which follows function; it was not invented by architects.

I gained even greater insight into the intricacies of structural biology when another professor in the department, John Enders, tutored me privately. We spent hours together examining three dimensional models of proteins. I even helped him build some of these models.

(Many years into the future, that experience helped me guide my daughter as she designed and assembled sprawling sculptures, some dozens of feet long, of actual protein structures—here's a picture of a sculpture she created for the Biopolis in Singapore, which shows the active part of a SARS cell, a coronavirus very similar to the one that caused the COVID-19 pandemic!)

With Professor Enders it was always hands-on learning, creating models to replicate a precision that the human eye by itself cannot detect. Each protein is specified by a gene. A gene carries instructions for a miniscule three dimensional object that does the work to make chemicals for the cells in your body. As I like to say: our bodies are made up of nanomachines. So is every tree in a redwood forest, some standing taller than three hundred feet.

(Later, I had the wild opportunity to work in the same laboratory where Professor Enders' uncle, John Franklin Enders, had first isolated the polio virus in the late 1940s. *This* John Enders was known by then as "The Father of Modern Vaccines." I sat in his chair! It wasn't the comfiest chair in the world, but it was still a thrill. I used the same bio-containment hood in which he grew the first polio viruses in various tissue cultures. That discovery, for which he shared the Nobel Prize in 1954, would lead to the mass production of the Salk and Sabin vaccines mentioned in Chapter 1. I was in awe, knowing the terror and disruption polio inflicted when I was a boy, and inspired to understand these viruses and follow in John Enders's footsteps as best I could.)

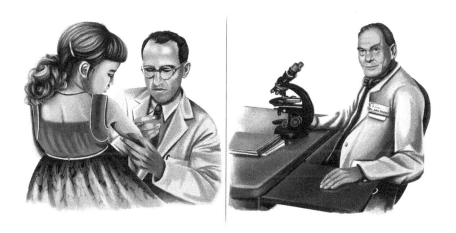

Jonas Salk and John Enders, two superheroes who gave me back my childhood freedom with their polio vaccines

Material science is approaching this same cellular precision, creating tiny machines designed to integrate with our bodies. Effective medicines work at this level to accelerate the power of proteins *or* inhibit *or* alter their capacity to achieve a specific physiological change. Scientists in synthetic biology use a similar approach to create new materials from different types of products. Create gasoline from sugar? Yep. Generate cannabinoids from sugar? Yes. If I were beginning my career now, scanning the horizon for new opportunities in science, I would give synthetic biology careful consideration.

This was the most advanced coursework you could do in physical chemistry. I was increasingly confident over those months that I could handle the physical chemistry part of being a scientist.

***

Harvard graduate students have the privilege of auditing undergraduate courses—in other words sitting in on the class, sopping up the knowledge, and never needing to turn in homework! With Boston's icy winter closing in, I preferred to hang out in the warm lecture halls to pass the time between my morning classes. I decided to audit whatever course was scheduled at that time. That course turned out to be an introduction to...drumroll please...molecular biology. A brilliant associate professor was teaching. Instead of lecturing, Walter Gilbert, a young University of Cambridge physics PhD, assigned students current papers from scientific journals, then led us through them, tearing apart the authors' methods and conclusions. *Whoa.* I was amazed. This struck me as basic training in critical thinking at the highest level. Above all else, Gilbert valued examination and asking questions. This was my kind of guy! His process looked a bit like this:

First, examine details from the experiments:

"What methods did these researchers use to get their results?" he would ask. "Are you confident you could follow these same methods in the lab and get the same results? Are the details precise, exhaustive?"

Next, pull apart the results:

"Were these answers meaningful? Were they statistically significant, or simply a minimal adjustment to what was already known?"

Finally, assess the conclusions:

"Were the authors' interpretations logical, based on all we know? Were the speculations they drew from the data reasonable? What other interpretations might be equally valid, or more persuasive?"

Not your average yes/no kind of conundrums. No, these questions made you think. Though my brain hurt from time to time, I felt useful. I felt like I was *actively* participating in the data, not just reading about it. Wally Gilbert's analytical approach ever since has been mine. Analyze the tools used to produce the data; eye the data critically; be precise and cautious interpreting even the most reliable data; reality may lurk at unimagined depths.

These are the essentials of scientific investigation. You can believe *the data* when an experiment is done well, but you do not have to believe that *the interpretation* is beyond question. Data is data, conclusions are theories. Wally drove home the point that misinterpretation happens more often than believed, even in papers in scientific journals. I'd tasted a bit of this in my Mars research with Pimentel. It was fascinating to see it in the world of molecular biology too.

Analyze the tools used to produce the data; eye the data critically; be precise and cautious interpreting even the most reliable data; reality may lurk at unimagined depths.

I was convinced from all I'd learned in Gilbert's class that molecular biology would progress rapidly. "Not only is his approach an awesome, but this new field of molecular biology is going to transform medicine," I thought. The implications for the future of medicine and human health were staggering. "Our bodies are made of genes!" I kept thinking, brain a-buzz, "and so molecular biology will be a very powerful tool."

***

As the end of the semester was coming to a close; so was my window for deciding whether to enter Harvard Medical School (to become a doctor) or to pursue my PhD. A guidance counselor in medical school admissions advised me to "talk to our top scientists" for advice. Well, don't mind if I do.

When I walked into the lab for my first interview arranged by the admissions office, an elaborate experiment was unfolding. A monkey was fixed to a chair, his eyes propped open and staring at a black bar on a white screen. An electrode connected to a microphone emerged from the monkey's shaved skull. Two men in white lab coats sat a few feet away. The taller of the two men—let's call him Heights—turned to me. "Watch this!" he said. The other man turned a nob and the black bar began to rotate slowly. When the angle of the rotating black bar reached precisely 7.5 degrees, an amplifier emitted a rapid series of clicks. As the angle shifted, the clicking volume rose or fell. "Look!"

Heights was psyched, smiling and nearly jumping up and down. He explained to me what the experiment—an historic event in science as it turned out—was proving. "The brain is pre-wired to respond to specific forms." Fourteen years later in 1981, these two men, David Hubel and Torsten Wiesel, received the Nobel Prize in Physiology or Medicine for their discoveries around information processing in the visual system.

Still energized from what we had witnessed, David Hubel sat me down in his cluttered office and listened carefully as I explained why I was there, paused for a moment, then in a quiet voice began to speak.

"I know something about your dilemma. I am a doctor who loves science. I thought I could do both. I am a doctor; I am a scientist. I am also a husband and a father," he continued. "For me, that is one too many responsibilities...If I had to do it again, I would devote all my time to science and family. I suggest you ask yourself a question I wish I had asked when I was your age: Are you compelled, really driven, to place your hands on a sick person to heal them? If so, then and only then, you should become a doctor."

He went on, "I see from your background you love science. Let me give you my opinion. You can do more for human health through science than you ever can as a doctor."

Thinking back on this now, I might have been a bit stunned by his candor. I nodded often but kept silent. Afterwards, I thanked him for his time and advice, then left his endearingly messy office. But there was no doubt: his words hit me like a thunderbolt.

Did I like being around sick people? No, frankly. I could get squeamish at that time in my life around the sick. Plus, I sometimes felt traumatized thinking back to my mother's illnesses that I'd witnessed at such a young age. And did I like the idea of putting my hands inside someone's body? Oof, no! I knew I never would be a good surgeon because my hands did not work always at my command. I'm ambidextrous (which means I have equal capabilities in both my left and right hand) and while this probably contributes to having an agile, flexible mind, it is not good for eye-hand coordination. You need fine motor skills to stitch someone up properly. In a flash, I imagined an incorrect, sloppy suture, my fault, someone else's life. The thought shook me.

I saw clearly now that my path should be a life devoted to healing *through science*, not medicine. Within a few days, I formally declined Harvard Medical School's offer to enroll to become a doctor.

I tell this story to reinforce for you that there are always surprises in life, so it's best to keep your mind open to many possibilities. Maybe you start off high school passionate about the bassoon, but by college, you realize your strengths sit elsewhere. Maybe you begin as a poet, and end up an accountant. Whatever your path(s), I suggest you always seek advice from those you respect, and always check in with yourself: where can I push my boundaries? Where should I honor my limitations? Science or no science, I encourage you to ask these questions, try to answer them, and Super PV your way into a life of meaning, purpose, and possibly monkeys.

There are always surprises in life, so it's best to keep your mind open to many possibilities.

***

Months after deciding to do my PhD thesis in molecular biology, I asked Wally Gilbert if I could work in his laboratory as a graduate student. Alas, it was full so I spent the summer working in another lab, learning basic but important microbiology techniques and generally sharpening my chops for when I could apply again to work in Gilbert's lab. When that time came, I had to interview with James D. Watson (known, affably, as Jim), one of the world's most celebrated scientists. I had no idea what to expect, and that might have been a good thing. When I interviewed for the position, I found it difficult to finish the answer to even one of his questions before he jumped in and asked another. But I must have done okay.

Soon, I was exactly where I wanted to be: admitted to a lab stocked with many of the world's finest scientists. I would be working with Watson—a few years prior, in 1962, had shared the Nobel Prize for his co-discovery with Francis Crick of the double helix structure of DNA— and the brilliant Gilbert, also destined for a Nobel Prize. Gulp.

In the entire history of science, I can confidently say that Jim Watson ranks as one of the greatest contributors to human welfare and knowledge, one of the greatest scientists of all time. In coming centuries, his name will be uttered alongside the names of the greats— Archimedes, Galileo, Newton, Darwin, Marie Curie, and Einstein. And maybe you, too.

Watson's discoveries with Francis Crick are profound, and with enormous consequences for our lives. Jim Watson answered an age old question: What is inheritance? The implications of that discovery for life and health will reverberate through the ages. More than any of his peers, he established the field of molecular biology as a discipline in the United States and around the world. What he opened up for medicine, for business, and for our curiosity amazes me. It did back then and it still does today. Maybe now more than ever.

Working for Watson and Wally Gilbert in their Harvard molecular biology lab was like learning at the feet of Plato and Aristotle. Learning to fly from Superman, learning to spider from Spiderman, you get the picture. They taught me the importance of *how to choose* and solve an important problem, then move on to the next. They showed me how to understand the deep implications of my work, and how to create that impact.

A decade before I joined the lab, Jim Watson and Francis Crick discovered the scientific answer to one of life's most fundamental questions: How does like beget like? Why, for example, do family members share the same features? My sister and I have almost identical cheeks; my brother and I have the same elbows. Why? The answer lay in the structure of DNA. Watson and Crick found that DNA comprises two strands twisted about each other, the now iconic double helix. Each strand is a perfect mold for the other. As the two strands separate, one defines the precise structure of the other, yielding from the original form two identical copies; and built into each strand are the instructions to make proteins—the micro machines that make life, in a word: *work.*

Jim Watson and Francis Crick

At the time I joined, the goal of the Watson-Gilbert lab was to explore how this process for making proteins happened. And to accomplish this goal, they encouraged collaboration and creativity. Each graduate student had responsibilities and freedoms similar to professors. We would choose our research topic. We would order what we needed to conduct experiments and decide the best approach. It was on us to design our experiments, which we did mostly by learning from one another. The lab was chockablock with intelligent, motivated students, many of whom would become lifelong friends and colleagues.

Though the lab was full of excitement and important work, there were also some challenges. There were mistakes, dead-ends, and disappointment. Every superhero has his kryptonite, right? But challenges are the building blocks of learning, I reasoned, despite the frustrations I often felt. I thought back to my early home experiments with bacteria, which sent my dad to the hospital. *Woops* moments are built into the fabric of this work, but boy do they sting.

After working in the Watson-Gilbert lab, I spent a summer at Cold Spring Harbor Laboratory (also run by Jim Watson). I was excited to be heading to Cold Spring Harbor, which was one of the most widely known and well-respected biomedical research facilities both then and now. Over the years, the lab has been home to numerous Nobel Prize winners. One of them, Barbara McClintock, was working there when I arrived, always willing to talk about her work, even to young graduate students like me. McClintock was the woman who discovered "jumping genes" —a fun way of describing a class of genetic elements that can jump to different locations within a genome. By the time I showed up, she had already made this important discovery, though the scientific community had laughed at her findings and ridiculed her early results. But even in the face of that resistance, McClintock never gave up. Instead, she continued working away quietly in the Cold Spring Lab, conducting experiments and generating evidence that only reinforced her initial conclusions.

McClintock had a penetrating intelligence and was ever open to new ideas. She understood the implications of her findings in the broadest sense and knew all too well that for many her results, which ran counter to the prevailing theories on genetics, came too soon. "One must await the right time for conceptual change," she once said. And so she did. Eventually, the rest of the scientific community caught up. In 1983, more than 30 years after she published her initial findings, she was awarded the Nobel Prize in Physiology or Medicine, the first solo female winner of the award.

McClintock's "jumping gene" discovery continues to inspire scientists today, helping them answer questions to some of the toughest challenges the world is facing...including one I know you're well aware of, COVID-19. For a long time, doctors and scientists couldn't figure out why patients who had recovered from COVID still produced viral RNA and tested positive even though they felt fine. In 2021, a group of scientists finally figured it out—it was a "jumping gene" that did it! SARS-CoV-2 uses a jumping gene to integrate into our DNA, so even though a patient recovers from the disease, their DNA still has enough of the virus' genetic coding integrated into it that people continue to test positive for the disease itself. An important discovery that would never have happened without McClintock's early work.

Her legacy is one of uncommon persistence in the face of adversity. It was a lesson I'd soon be learning myself, though in my case the adversity was of my own making. I had come to Cold Spring to continue experiments on DNA, particularly regarding the way in which bacteria copies DNA for replication. But I was young and still a bit immature, so I went a bit rogue with my experiments. I wanted to do my own thing—I'm sure you feel like that at times—and I failed to take direction. This resulted in a significant setback in the lab's progress; other labs had found the data that we were trying to publish first. And it was clearly my fault. From *woops* to *oh no* to *"get out!"* I was asked to leave Cold Spring and return to the lab at Harvard.

"Your scientific career is not over," Watson reassured me, "go back and work hard." Humbled, I took this as a lesson: *I am just an apprentice, with no more rights than a medieval stone mason learning his craft.*

***

Sometimes other scientists and students made mistakes, too, which was almost as troubling to endure. Though the graduate lab atmosphere was mostly supportive, often opinions would differ, theories would be disproved, and feelings would get hurt. I had to remind myself: these heroes are humans, and these are some pretty high stakes. Studying the ways in which life functions (or doesn't) is nothing to sneeze at; these tests and experiments not only study life itself, but have the possibility to change our understanding of it, too.

I thought about all this as I outlined a potential thesis project revolving around, yes, you guessed it: bacteria. Our gut bacteria (sidebar: you have about one hundred *trillion...*!) undergo repeated cycles of feast or famine. After a meal they are flooded with nutrients. During feast time they reproduce wildly, doubling every forty minutes. During famine, however, our bacteria are chilling out, totally idle. They do not reproduce, but they survive by scavenging for whatever few nutrients might be floating about in our gut. When they are growing, bacteria produce all the proteins necessary to make more bacteria. In idle mode they make an entirely different set of proteins which are suitable for the scavenging life cycle. My thought was, "Might understanding how a bacterium switches from feast to famine, from growth to scavenging, reveal a profound answer?"

Andrew Travers, a postdoctoral fellow from England who had worked in the Watson-Gilbert lab before I arrived, thought the answer was yes. He had made important suggestions regarding rapidly growing bacteria and how it relates to **ribosomal RNA**, DNA, **gene expression**, and **cell differentiation**. He posited that a certain substance was needed (he called it the *psi* factor, which, I admit, now sounds a bit like the name of a reality television show) to copy RNA and replicate genes and proteins. I wasn't skeptical, but I was curious to discover more: what is this *psi* factor, *really*, why not identify it in pure form, and then go on to unravel exactly how it works? Travers had not actually identified the *psi* factor. He had only shown the effect from using an extract from growing cells that contained many differences substances. I saw an opportunity. Thesis project, here I come.

Might understanding how a bacterium switches from feast to famine, from growth to scavenging, reveal a profound answer?

Over the next several weeks, I purified the DNA from E. coli bacteria, added the ingredients needed to make RNA, and measured whether or not I had made ribosomal

RNA. The answer was entirely unexpected. The experiments showed that I was able to make ribosomal RNA *with no added factors*. I double and triple checked, and more. I even developed an entirely new way to detect ribosomal RNA. The same result every time: no extra factors were needed. How was I to purify *psi* factor if it was not needed to make ribosomal RNA, after all? If my observations were true, they would contradict what Travers had found, which by now was widely accepted as a major scientific advance.

Jim Watson immediately grasped the issue. "This is so important," he said, "that you should do the same experiments in Andrew's lab under his supervision." Travers was back in England at this point, so this would mean another—but very different kind of— journey for me. Graciously, Travers welcomed me to his lab and even hosted me in his home. But the atmosphere was uncomfortable. If the experiment confirmed my results, not his, the impact on his reputation would be… well, we did not talk about that. We did not talk much at all outside the lab.

It was springtime. For two weeks we traveled back and forth to his lab through the blooming English countryside. Honeysuckle and cornflower rolled by but we had other life forms on our mind. At the lab, Andrew would collect samples from my experiments, then place them in a machine to read the results. He would know the answers. I would not. Cue the mystery and intrigue.

Wally and Jim had agreed that I should go directly from England when my work with Andrew finished to present my results at a prestigious scientific conference in New Hampshire; this would be my first real scientific debut addressing world experts. I repeat: GULP.

Just before I left England, Andrew handed me a sealed envelope with a letter he had written inside. "After your talk, have this letter read," he told me. "Do not open it." "OK…" I replied, madly curious.

Andrew's letter was burning a hole in my pocket, but I kept my word. When my turn came to speak at the conference, I handed the sealed letter to the moderator before I began and asked him to read it to the sixty scientists in the audience, all experts in the field, after I finished. "You have seen the data," I semi-confidently announced, all-star molecular biologists in the front row staring right at me, "I do not confirm the Travers result regarding *psi* factor. No additional factor is required to make ribosomal RNA."

The audience was silent, but only for a moment. Then, the all-stars piped up, and disagreed; they'd all conducted similar experiments and concluded the opposite. From the downturn of their brows to the upturn of their voices, they did *not* seem happy with me or my findings. What was I going to say? I was a young graduate student presenting at my first major conference. Three legendary giants directly contradicted me. But back at the Harvard lab, we'd been trained to defend independent research. This was my moment to stand strong, not to get intimidated, or worse yet, sad. I held my ground. "I did these experiments. I did not make up this data. These are the results. There has to be an explanation, and I am happy to explore it further with you."

The letter? What about the sealed Travers letter? The conference organizer stood, facing the audience.

"We have a letter here that Bill brought with him in a sealed envelope. The letter is from Andrew Travers. Bill repeated these experiments in England under Andrew's direct supervision. Even Bill does not know the results of their work."

This was my moment to stand strong, not to get intimidated, or worse yet, sad.

The organizer opened the envelope and began reading: "To my dear colleagues. I oversaw the experiments Bill did in my laboratory in Cambridge. I deeply regret to inform you that you *are* able to make ribosomal RNA without *psi* factor."

Again, silence, followed by a few barely audible gasps. Then the session ended. No one came forward to offer congratulations; I wasn't looking for pats on the back, but some recognition would have felt good. It always feels good to be recognized for good work, right? Well, it turns out that in some cases of science, people dislike it when a popular hypothesis is disproved. It's tough to realize that something they learned is wrong. There's a ripple effect, too, when theories are disproven; as I spoke in New Hampshire, dozens of new grant proposals based on the *psi* hypothesis were under review. Now, with Andrew's confirmation of my results, few if any of those proposals would be funded.

What about Andrew Travers? Andrew admitted he made a mistake, then carried on. If my memory is correct, he even published a note confirming my results. A man of high integrity, Travers continued his research for many years. To my mind, Andrew is an excellent scientist and a fine human being. And yep, he made a mistake. That happens, even to superheroes. In science (and cooking and dancing and puppy-training and…) you will have disappointments.

My biggest disappointment at the time was that I'd need another thesis idea. More than two years into the PhD program and now I had to go back to square one.

Disproving theories does not earn you any points at Harvard. The standard at Harvard is: What big important problem have you *solved*? Okay, Harvard, I thought, I'm up for the task; I will solve a big important problem!

Still hooked on feast and famine, I was determined to stay with the problem. How do different cells read different RNAs and replicate? What causes ribosomal RNA to be made, or not made? "Travers had gotten it wrong, but I will get it right," I thought. "I will create a system in a test tube that mimics starvation. That will be my thesis."

A problem with earlier experiments might have been that we all were using unrealistically *diluted* (watered down) forms of purified bacteria extracts that do not mimic natural conditions. Highly *concentrated* whole extracts, I reasoned, should better replicate the behavior of the living organism. I'd recently learned about a scientist who'd demonstrated that two small molecules accumulate in bacteria that's in starvation mode. The scientist, Michael Cashel, called these molecules *magic spots one and two*. Kind of cute sounding, right?

"If I can create conditions in a test tube that really mimic conditions of a living cell," I contemplated, "the starved system should mirror Cashel's results and produce magic spot in a test tube." Wally Gilbert loved my idea, and gave me critical advice regarding my process of concentrating the bacterial extracts. I started my experiments immediately, typically working from 10:00 a.m. to midnight. Most of the work required removing stray **amino acids** from the concentrate. I knew I was on the right track when amino acids I added to the extract *restored* protein synthesis after I had removed the free amino acids. Removing free amino acids *stopped* the synthesis; adding amino acids restarted it. Red light, green light.

Late one afternoon, I added something called GTP (Guanosine triphosphate, which provides the power for protein synthesis) to the mix at the location Wally had coached me to use—with and without amino acids. After letting it cook for half an hour in a **centrifuge**—perhaps the longest thirty minutes of my life—I placed a drop of the reaction on filter paper, placed the filter paper over an X-ray film, and left for a quick dinner. Guy's gotta eat.

When I returned to the lab to develop the film...Eureka! Score! Huzzah! YESSS! Two spots on the film! These were the magic spots, one and two, right before my eyes. I had made magic spot in a test tube! And if I had not followed Wally's advice, I would have missed the big discovery. This story shows how working under a brilliant mentor can make a huge difference. The feeling I had in that moment was incredible. Finally, I was certain I had the subject for my thesis: making magic spot.

"Jim! Jim, I made magic spot in a test tube!" It was early the next morning and I had reached Jim Watson in Cold Spring Harbor. "Ahhh," he replied, with just a touch of delight. He did not offer any praise or ask questions. "Now," this world famous superhero of modern science added, "you are going to be a scientist."

Working under a brilliant mentor can make a huge difference. The feeling I had in that moment was incredible.

In a flash I saw the future. "I know I can take the system apart and discover exactly how magic spot is made. This would be a breakthrough." I had no time to lose. The race was on to carefully document my magic spot experiments, then write it up. Other scientists were trying to figure out how magic spot was made, and a little bit of healthy competition turned up the heat.

My lab partner and I worked as hard as we could for nine months, literally living in the lab twenty-four hours a day, sleeping (and snoring, apparently) only during the brief periods we let the reactions cook—often twenty or thirty minutes. Exhausted—but somehow also energized—we rushed home only on Sunday afternoons to do laundry (boring!), then returned to the lab by nightfall.

I learned so much about myself and about science during that time. It felt wonderful to be so focused on my work—anxiety begone! Well, never gone entirely but definitely redirected into something positive. Through those long days and nights in the lab, every bit of my being—my emotions, my intellect, my physical activity—was hyper-focused on only one thing. This is what creativity demands: obsession and total laser focus to the exclusion of all else. I envisioned myself as a fighter pilot closing in on a target, my hand reaching out to switch off all external stimuli: social life, politics, friends, family... everything, to focus on only one goal.

Through those long days and nights in the lab, every bit of my being—my emotions, my intellect, my physical activity—was hyper-focused on only one thing. This is what creativity demands: obsession and total laser focus to the exclusion of all else.

The experience changed me forever. I never again fretted about working long hours. (I did...er...have to be admitted to a hospital for nearly a week after the first nine months—exhaustion, dehydration—but I recovered quickly!) I had confidence that I could face the rigors of the scientific life. I could focus and succeed. I continued my experiments until I had enough data to publish a second scientific paper, write my thesis, and complete my Harvard PhD. YESSS!

***

Surely, you've gathered by now that being a scientist is demanding at times. This comes with the territory. You fail; you compete with your colleagues and friends. Sometimes you work for years, not knowing if your experiments will yield an important, or trivial, answer. But, believe me, the feelings you have after discovering an important answer that will benefit millions of people are worth every step of the struggle.

Not long after receiving my PhD, I had a surprising conversation that summed up the mental toughness scientists require. Harry Eagle, a physician, big time medical scientist, and leader of the Albert Einstein College of Medicine was a tireless advocate for biomedical research. One morning, we met over eggs and bacon at a retreat for promising young scientists, organized by a foundation that was financially supporting all of our research. Harry Eagle was the foundation's chairman.

"So you want to be a scientist," he began.

"Of course," I said. "That is why I am here."

Harry Eagle had a point to make, so he continued, "You know, only young men and women who have been told by their parents that they are God's gift to the world—and who believe what they are told—can be scientists. We all face too many failures and too few successes to persevere without rock solid self-confidence."

"No problem," I replied. "I believe what my mother told me."

***

My years in the Watson-Gilbert lab prepared me for the challenges and realities of a life in science. It was tough, but it was excellent preparation for what was ahead. With my Harvard biophysics doctorate in hand (doctorate is a common term for PhD), I would move a few miles down the Charles River and be among the first to leap into the new DNA research at MIT that would ignite the biotechnology revolution.

Being at the top of any profession is demanding and competitive. Success demands many talents. Ambition, desire for achievement, and social and political awareness are critical. Above all is perseverance: the ability to keep striving despite setbacks, always with your goal in mind.

The feelings you have after discovering an important answer that will benefit millions of people are worth every step of the struggle.

And remember, if you are going to pick a problem to solve, pick an important one. It's as hard to solve a small problem as it is to solve a big problem. When you follow a recipe, it can be a good recipe or a bad recipe, either will take as much time and effort. You can end up with a bad tasting mix or a delicious cake. It takes the same amount of work. May as well make (and eat!) the cake.

CHAPTER 5

More Genes, Jims, And Johns

In the early 1970s animal viruses were the only way molecular biologists could study the complex biology of higher organisms. The ability to work with individual human genes came later in the decade, but virologists at this time already were making huge strides in understanding how viruses invade healthy cells and infect. You're probably used to a lot of virus-talk, thanks to COVID-19. But COVID-19 is not our first time at the viral rodeo. Viruses have been with us forever.

A man name David Baltimore was at the forefront of our group of molecular biologists. Up until the late 1960s, his research had focused on the polio virus, which, as you'll remember, caused a global epidemic in the 1950s and a whole lot of fear in the Haseltine household. By the late 1960s, David had moved on to study viruses known to cause cancer in animals and suspected of causing cancers in humans too. I respected David for his work on the polio virus and for his antiwar activism; he had concerns (as did I) over the American government's potential abuse of science in waging the Vietnam War.

By 1973, David had made a major discovery: some of these viruses contained an unusual **enzyme**, one that copies RNA into DNA. The discovery illuminated the little understood process of how viruses multiply. Also, the discovery propelled David's laboratory at MIT to the forefront of animal virus research, exactly where I wanted to be. He welcomed me into his lab and, with his support and mentorship, I soon received funding for my postdoctoral research.

As far back as 1911, the dawn of virus discoveries, a pathologist and virologist, Peyton Rous (cool name alert), identified a virus that induced tumors in chickens. He described these as a "filterable virus." In the early 1950s, Ludwig Gross (ditto) showed that these viruses induced leukemia, a cancer of blood-making tissues such as bone marrow, in mice. Others showed they induced cancers in other animals, including cats, cattle and even monkeys. But what about humans? Do viruses cause cancers in humans? By the late 1960s, viruses were known to cause lymphoma, liver cancer and cervical cancer. If viruses are a major cause of cancer, could an anticancer vaccine be possible?

If viruses are a major cause of cancer, could an anticancer vaccine be possible?

There was great enthusiasm for answering that question. Mary Lasker, a powerful voice championing more funding for science in the White House and the halls of Congress, was among the most prominent advocates. (Scientific research is best performed with congressional support; running all those labs and tests is expensive. But the payoff can be huge—life-saving, in fact.) The National Cancer Act approved by Congress in 1971 had pumped new money into the search for viruses that might cause cancer. The part of the act known as the Special Virus Cancer Program covered an entire family of viruses that were now known, thanks to David Baltimore's discovery, as "retroviruses." As I weighed my options in the spring of 1973 for a postdoctoral fellowship, the field of retroviruses was red hot. (And just to zoom out for some non-sciencey context, because even I need a break sometimes: this was the same year that FedEx became a thing.)

***

Zooming out even further, let's take a quick zip around the globe to Copenhagen (the capital city of Denmark), where I spent a summer as a visiting professor in the months after finishing in the Watson-Gilbert Lab. The Copenhagen lab was well-known. Jim Watson had spent a short time there in the early 1950s before joining Francis

Crick for their DNA double helix discoveries. Copenhagen was Beautiful-with-a-capital-B. This was my first exposure to life in Scandinavia and a balm for me emotionally, the first time I felt that my values were well-matched to a nation's culture. Most people opposed the Vietnam War. Most believed in the equality of men and women. Most displayed respect for all with no regard to appearances or personal wealth. A robust social safety net protected everyone, young and old.

Children were prized, a sentiment obvious in even the smallest details. For example, every "polser" (read: hot dog) stand was fronted by tiny steps that enabled very young children to step up for a look inside. I had never seen anything like that in the United States. Also, Danish men played a more central role in family life than in America. One day, when I saw an injured child run for comfort to her father, not her mother, I was pleased and surprised, another delightful vignette from a relaxed and happy summer... a year short of my thirtieth birthday... when I was so in tune with the prevailing philosophy. Not in conflict with it.

(Who else is in the mood for a polser?)

I was a first time parent by then, too. My daughter, Mara, was born during my PhD studies at Harvard. My son, Alex, would arrive soon, not long after I landed in the

David Baltimore lab at MIT. I found being a parent to be one of life's greatest pleasures. I had the special situation many scientists enjoy of being able to manage my time however I wished, so I was able to take my kids to museums and other neat places whenever I wanted. Even better, they came with me on each of my research trips outside the United States, first to Denmark, and later to Japan and France. Now that I am a grandparent, I have all the fun of reliving these wonderfully uplifting times with my grandkids.

***

Now, back to science and David Baltimore.

David's work was based on the work of a scientist in Wisconsin, Howard Temin, who had developed the idea that the RNA of some viruses is converted first to DNA, which is then used to produce new viral RNA. (Before, many believed that that genetic information cannot be transferred back from protein to **nucleic acid**.) Howard and David both published the discovery that polio viruses contain an enzyme that does just that, copies RNA into DNA. David gave the enzyme the name *reverse transcriptase*. (The enzyme causes transcribing of genetic information in reverse; hence, reverse transcriptase.)

Ta-daaahh! I was in the lab when David took the call. The news was spectacular: he and Howard Temin would share the 1975 Nobel Prize in Physiology or Medicine with the Italian-American virologist Renato Dulbecco! All three had a hand in the discoveries of reverse transcriptase. Everyone in the lab was jubilant. David arrived smiling ear to ear, as relaxed and happy as I'd ever seen him. His physical prize, a solid gold medal, has the profile of Alfred Nobel on one side and the award citation on the other. When I had the chance to hold the medal after David returned from the ceremony in Stockholm, I was awed and delighted. I was also slightly scared I'd drop it.

You might be wondering, Who was Renato Dulbecco?? Well, he had mentored Howard as a PhD candidate at the California Institute of Technology and David as a research associate at the Salk Institute. In other words, he was the most important coach at that point in their young careers as virologists. This is an example of how science is passed down from hand to hand, with young scientists learning from great masters and becoming masters themselves, too. Science is one of the few aspects of modern life that retains the guild system; you are trained by master craftsmen and women; you in turn train the next generation of master craftsmen and women, who train the next generation, and so it goes. Many scientists working to discover treatments and vaccines for COVID-19 are my former colleagues and students, and students of my students. In this regard, too, I consider myself to be the scientific grandson of two über-masters, Salvador Luria and Max Delbruck (the 1969 Nobel Prize winners for their discoveries on the replication mechanism and the genetic structure of viruses); Jim Watson learned directly from them, and as we know, I learned directly from Jim Watson.

Science is one of the few aspects of modern life that retains the guild system; you are trained by master craftsmen and women; you in turn train the next generation of master craftsmen and women, who train the next generation, and so it goes.

***

At Baltimore's MIT lab, I would go on to investigate retrovirus replication. To this, I employed basic techniques of what we today call **gene-splicing** and **recombinant DNA**. I was not alone in my pursuit; Daniel Nathans at Johns Hopkins and Paul Berg at Stanford were learning how to cut and splice DNA. Werner Arber, a Swiss microbiologist and geneticist, discovered enzymes that protect bacteria in two ways: by chopping up the DNA of infecting viruses to restrict the virus growth, and by modifying the bacteria's *own* DNA to defend against attack. What this proved was that a fragment of DNA from a bacteria could be cut and joined to a piece of human DNA.

Nathans and Berg demonstrated that a bacteria would copy the new hybrid DNA *as if it were a natural part of its own DNA*. These discoveries had big-time implications for modern science as well as modern medicine. Bacteria with human DNA spliced into its **genome** could produce functioning human proteins. This immediately raised the possibility that proteins vital for modern medicine, such as **insulin and human growth hormone**, could be sourced not only from the human body. What Nathans, Berg and Arber had discovered were the foundations of **genetic engineering**. Proteins could be *engineered* to grow in bacteria. Incredible stuff.

Meantime, I was hunkering down in the lab (as I do) working on virus replication experiments; I knew I could manipulate the viral DNA more easily in test tubes than viral RNA, something no one else had attempted. It was an exciting several months, imagining how my discoveries might improve human health. I always checked back in with myself: *Hey Bill, are you working toward your goal? Are you pursuing your passion, your purpose? Are you happy? Tired?* Yes, yes, yes, yes, and yes. *Okay, then, keep going.*

The physical lab was small, and packed full with David's rapidly growing roster of fellows and other researchers, most of whom were funded by new grants from the federal National Cancer Act. I was allotted one square meter of lab bench, with one small drawer that I shared with four others. Have you ever had to share a drawer? It's not easy! At one point, I decided to clear space for mixing substances on my small work space by rigging a tray and suspending it from my neck. This actually was more fun/functional than it sounds.

We all knew exactly what each of us was working on, precisely how we were doing it, and how to negotiate sharing essential equipment. Eventually we moved into a new building—a renovated candy factory on the edge of campus—which seemed palatial. David was given more than half of one floor. I had an entire lab bench and desk to myself! No candy though…

One morning, finally, my gene splicing experiments were ready to begin. The goal would be groundbreaking, if we could achieve it: to copy viral RNA into DNA, then insert that DNA into a bacterium to copy *that* DNA. The ultimate copycat.

An ice bucket with ten test tubes, each filled with a chemical solution, was next to me at my bench. Just before I planned to start, David asked me to wait a few hours. What!? Why?! I noticed Paul Berg and several other scientists enter a conference room not twenty feet away.

Now I had to wait. I could hear them talking heatedly but could not make out the words. I had no sense of what was happening. Cue the mystery and intrigue...and the worry. After three long hours, with the ice melting in my bucket, David opened the door and walked straight to me.

"The experiment is off," he said.

Just like that. Several months of work and research down the drain. My buoyant expectations for a great scientific revolution, dashed.

"We need to invite many more scientists, ethicists and lawyers and figure out guidelines any scientist will have to follow for research in recombinant DNA," he continued. "We have decided to hold a more formal meeting."

It is likely that my experiments would have led to exciting discoveries and professional opportunities. Other biologists soon confirmed that the role of RNA splicing in gene replication is similar to a film editor's: it eliminates unnecessary elements (the boring scenes of the movie) of a DNA molecule and connects essential parts into a completed segment that matches the gene segments. In fact, the RNA splicing process turns out to be a major distinction between simple organisms such as bacteria and more complex organisms such as plants and pets and you and me.

Would my genetic engineering set loose a molecular Frankenstein monster into the world? I didn't think so… but I understood the concerns. This level of research and gene manipulation was brand new, and safety rules needed to be established. Remember, we're talking high stakes here. As it turned out, that meeting in our conference room was a prelude to what became requirements for any work funded by the National Institutes of Health and, eventually, those requirements were adopted as global standards.

The experiments I had planned for Dave's lab did not meet the requirements. You might have seen photos of people in bubble like protective gear working with dangerous viruses. Since the COVID-19 pandemic began, who hasn't?! That is what was required. Only a few places had such facilities. MIT's revamped candy factory was not one of them.

I was disappointed not to carry out my experiments as planned, but I remained confident and ready to rebound. I knew the value of persistence. Appreciate every experience and learn what you can. If one door closes, there are always others.

I knew the value of persistence. Appreciate every experience and learn what you can. If one door closes, there are always others.

I was still interested in studying how retroviruses replicate and how I might apply that knowledge to improve cancer, virus, and treatment research. So I continued to experiment, safely, with viral transfers between RNA and DNA. I had the help of an expert in the field—another Jim, Jim Dahlberg—out at the University of Wisconsin; I would conduct the experiments in Cambridge and then ship the substances in dry ice to Wisconsin for Jim to analyze. There was an unforeseen benefit of working with Jim D. As you might know, Wisconsin is famous for dairy. So, naturally, the University of Wisconsin has a renowned dairy science department, and Jim's lab was within a few steps of the department's creamery. Every time Jim shipped my package of test tubes in dry ice back to Cambridge, he added some experimental flavor of ice cream. Pumpkin pomegranate, anyone? I would not it. Pumpkin fudge or blueberry kiwi? Much tastier. My reciprocal offerings to Jim were whole frozen lobsters. So long as nobody got lobster flavored ice cream, it was a great arrangement.

All frozen treats aside, our tests yielded striking results that I continued to study and analyze after leaving David Baltimore's lab, and returning to Harvard where I was assigned my own lab (!) in the Sidney Farber Cancer Institute (later renamed the Dana-Farber Cancer Institute to honor the support of industrialist Charles A. Dana, who believed, like Sidney Farber, that there is "no such thing as a hopeless case"). There, alongside my research colleague—another John, John Coffin—we proved the unexpected: that viral RNA is copied *within* bacteria into DNA as *one continuous chain*; it was not copied with small fragments of DNA being linked together, as we'd thought. We also figured out that retrovirus genomes contain the same sequence of **nucleotides** at both ends. We named this *terminal redundancy*. I applied another new technique in recombinant DNA to show that the viral RNA is, indeed, copied into DNA as one continuous chain, from one end of the genome to the other. Boom, and boom.

***

So now that I've given you a lot of words and terms and lobsters to chew on, and now that I've walked you through the ups and downs of what went on in those labs, let's pause for a moment of reflection:

Young people making decisions about their careers are keenly tuned in to the opportunities available to them. So keep your eyes and ears wide open—opportunity may be hard to spot sometimes, but once you do, seize it. During my years working in research labs, the government's enthusiasm for science education created for me and my peers an abundance of mentors, programs, projects—and funding through my Harvard graduate studies. Then, as the implications of David Baltimore's stunning DNA discoveries and research on animal viruses reverberated, a new wave for human cancer research was forming at a perfect time for me. My advice to you is to think about what's particular to this current era, and how it might be opening doors for you,. Maybe you're interested in Artificial Intelligence or cryptocurrency? Maybe you're interested in sustainable energy? Or, coding for new apps? Now is the time to capitalize on those interests and seek out mentors and study programs. They certainly are out there.

Keep your eyes and ears wide open—opportunity may be hard to spot sometimes, but once you do, seize it.

Those two years in David Baltimore's lab were the highlight of my graduate and postdoctoral training. In the thirteen years since my first byline in the pages of *Science*, I had made significant contributions to biophysics and molecular biology. My graduate course studies had given me a deep understanding for what was known in physics and chemistry. Moreover, I appreciated how essential teamwork and collaboration are in advancing science. I had learned how to work with colleagues when we were crowded together in labs and when we were spread out across distant cities and countries.

As a medical scientist on the cusp of my career, I could see endless possibilities in my future. It was time to apply all that I had learned to the great questions of human health and disease. But, where should I go, and what exactly should I do?

CHAPTER 6

Jobs, Riddles, And Making A (Big) Difference

I'd had my fun; it was time to get a job. The prospect excited me—a career is what I'd been working toward all these years—but in a way I'd gotten used to being a student. Undergrad, graduate, followed by my postdoctoral research... it was cozy in academia. But all good things must end, yes? At least I'd developed enough of a skillset so I could begin my job hunt with the confidence and gusto of a high flying birthday balloon.

Balloons pop, however, as did my gusto when my very first job prospect—a faculty member for the biochemistry department back at Berkeley—was given to someone else before I even got a fair chance to apply. As with other disappointments, this got me down, but only to get up again. I was offered two jobs in New York, one at Albert Einstein College of Medicine in the Bronx and one at Sloan Kettering Memorial Cancer Hospital in Manhattan. But the job I ultimately accepted came along in an unusual manner. Jack Strominger was a biochemistry professor at Harvard's BioLabs on the same floor as Watson-Gilbert. You know all about Alexander Fleming, but Jack Strominger was also renowned for his penicillin related work— discovering in the 1960s *how* exactly it killed bacteria. From time to time he had invited me down the hall to speak with him and his students over lunch. One afternoon when I was at MIT, he called. "Bill, I see you are doing great work on retroviruses. Do you have time to stop by for another presentation and brown bag lunch sometime soon?"

I showed up in Jack's conference room in tattered blue jeans, tired and unshaved after an all-nighter in the lab. Brown bag lunch means informal, right? Wrong! Crowded around the table was the entire biophysics faculty—role models and Nobel Prize winners included (all closely shaved, and definitely not wearing denim). Not anything I had expected.

My presentation, it seemed obvious that morning, was an unofficial audition for a faculty position in the BioLabs. Jack called me the next day. "That was a great seminar. You knocked it out of the park. We were all excited and," he continued, "I have an offer for you."

What came next was totally unexpected and totally thrilling:

"You might know that I am the Chair of the Department of Biological Science across the river at the Sidney Farber Cancer Institute. (I did not.) The Farber has just been designated a comprehensive cancer center by the National Cancer Institute. My job…" he continued, "…is to recruit scientists that have an interest in medicine as well as science. I want you to join us. You will have your own lab right away and a much bigger one when we finish our new building. Tom Frei, Farber's president and one of the country's leading cancer doctors, and I are best friends. I told him about you, and he is excited. You will love him."

Then came the truly dazzling part, a professional role I had imagined ever since those initial studies on campus before my PhD research. Really, since my seventh grade frog project! I wanted to be at Harvard. I wanted to work closely with doctors in a teaching hospital. I wanted to learn about their problems, then research and apply what I learned to help cure cancer and other disease.

"You will work right beside leading cancer therapists and other researchers," Jack said. "Not only that, you can be a member of any Harvard Medical School department you want. You can teach if you want, too."

Wrapping up, he added, "We can give you startup research money. Your salary will be almost twice what we could give you at the BioLabs."

Whoa. I couldn't believe it. "Wow, that seems too good to be true," I said. After a pause, I added, "I do have one request…" To build a team of top researchers for a lab, I knew I would need funding for two postdoctoral assistants right away. With those two positions we could hopefully make some significant lab discoveries that would attract grant money to add more positions.

"Ye-e-e-s?" Jack's reply was cautious, and his pitch a little higher than normal.

I chuckled to myself, remembering that when a good fairy comes along you are granted at least one wish. My one wish then, to Jack: "I would like a guaranteed salary for two postdoctoral fellows for two years."

"Done!" he replied.

And just like that, my job search had ended. When you go hunting for your first job (or any job), a bad start right out of the gate (like mine) doesn't necessarily lead to a bad ending. For me the result couldn't have been better.

When you go hunting for your first job (or any job), a bad start right out of the gate (like mine) doesn't necessarily lead to a bad ending.

***

My early months as a young professor were exhilarating. I was free as a bee (a bee with a paycheck!)— free to choose which problems to solve, to hire whomever I wanted, and to work how and when I wanted. Harvard's expectations for new faculty are lofty but clear: be the best *in the world* at what you do and raise whatever funds you need to succeed. Up for the challenge, I vowed to use my skills and knowledge of molecular biology to make a difference to medicine. But how?

What follows is a journey of discovery. Asking questions, seeing where they lead. Trying this, trying that, always with the ultimate goal in mind—how will my work help heal the sick, how will my work help people in need? I could not see the path that lay ahead, but I knew my destination.

From my postdoctoral research in virus replication, I'd learned that one type of retrovirus grew in mice and caused leukemia, and another closely related strain of that same retrovirus did not. This sparked a question I wanted to pursue: Might understanding this difference lead to an understanding of the cause of human cancer?

I could not see the path that lay ahead, but I knew my destination.

I planned experiments and described them to my new postdoctoral fellows, Finn and Jack. Huddled together like soldiers of science, I advised Jack to inject the mice with viral strains and observe what happened. Finn would work in the lab creating DNA copies of the viruses. Meanwhile I pursued a different line of research, studying fundamental aspects of virus replication, and sought more talent to expand our studies. The experiments went well, leading to more research manuscripts, review articles and several more grants. As soon as Finn and Jack received independent funding from outside sources, I invited two more postdoctoral fellows to join the lab. It truly does take a village.

***

Richard Gardner, an English scientist, discovered that he could grow very early mouse **embryo cells** in the lab that, under the right conditions when planted in the womb of a female mouse, resulted in a pregnancy and birth of a fully functioning mouse. The newly born mouse was a *clone* of the parent. Holy. Moly.

Richard also described what happened to mouse embryo cells attached to the plastic surface of a petri dish: These cells transformed into many different kinds of tissues, nerve, kidney, heart muscle cells and more. *Holy. Moly.*

I was enthralled. Richard was demonstrating how animal embryo cells can be replicated in the lab! One of his students sent me some of the mouse embryo cells replicated in Richard's lab and I began to tinker with them, noting various changes when different chemicals and hormones were added. These early experiments were laying a foundation for what within a few decades would become known as the field of regenerative medicine: the science of restoring weakened or damaged cells to their normal function in the tissues or organs of humans or animal cells. (We'll talk more about regenerative medicine in Chapter 8.)

Maybe you've heard of Dolly the Sheep? She was the first cloned large animal, and Gardner's experiments led directly to her birth in 1996. Also she was named after Dolly Parton, who you should definitely listen to some time, if you haven't already. A hero not of science, but of country music. Well, I take that back; Dolly Parton donated one million dollars to the vaccine research and development for COVID-19, so far as I see it, she's up there in the ranks of science superheroes, too!

With Gardner's work in mind, my postdoctoral fellows and I continued our experiments with the mice and strains of retrovirus. When we noticed that one strain kept the mice healthy and the other made them sick with leukemia, we began to cut and paste, lopping up the strains and rearranging the DNA sequences to determine what exactly was making the mice sick, and when? We wondered: maybe infection depends on what kind of cells are receiving the virus.

Here we were getting at one of the big unsolved problems in biology in the 1980s: What makes one cell different from another? All cells contain the same information. However, the information they extract from DNA and the process within each cell by which specific genes are expressed is different. For that reason, in each cell, different parts of the DNA are read into different *RNAs*. How can the DNA that is the same in every cell give rise to so many different types of specialized cells?

I had been down this road before with colleagues at the Watson-Gilbert lab, searching without success for answers to what causes cells to express genes in different ways. But Finn, Jack and I were getting very close to a reason why.

And then....bingo! BIG INDEPENDENT DISCOVERY. My team of Dana-Farber research scientists discovered the answer: a *short* DNA sequence can determine in which type of cell RNA will be made! In other words, a short sequence of DNA causes all cells which carry the same genetic information to reproduce in *many different ways.* We named these short DNA sequences *tissue specific enhancers.* Today it is widely accepted that tissue specific enhancers explain a big part of what makes one cell different from another. Short sequences usually determine, in or near a gene, whether or not **RNA polymerase** can load onto DNA. That is how synthesis begins.

The question we asked—Why did one strain of virus cause cancer and not another?—did not lead immediately to a new understanding of human leukemia. But it did provide the first step for a multiyear effort by scientists around the world to understand how and when genes are regulated in health and disease. Our discovery was pivotal to our ability today to understand and treat cancer and other diseases.

Some of the most significant medical and scientific advances aren't just the result of hard work—though hard work definitely plays a part—but rather the result of an open mind and a willingness to pursue an answer, no matter where it takes you.

Oftentimes as a scientist, the questions you start off with don't always match the answers you find. Instead, your research leads you somewhere else, and sometimes that somewhere else is a wonderful new discovery. Some of the most significant medical and scientific advances aren't just the result of hard work—though hard work definitely plays a part—but rather the result of an open mind and a willingness to pursue an answer, no matter where it takes you.

***

Let me take a break from my own story and introduce you to a few more superheroes who can help me illustrate the point.

Have you ever heard of CRISPR-Cas9? (It sounds like a character from Star Wars, doesn't it?). CRISPR-Cas9 is a new technology with the potential to transform our ability to cure disease. I'm simplifying a bit, but the way CRISPR works is to take the genes that make people sick and repair the parts that cause the sickness. In other words, levelling the genetic playing field. With this approach, entire diseases could be eradicated in just one or two generations.

It's possible that we wouldn't know about CRISPR-Cas9's potential if it weren't for the hard work of two scientists, Jennifer Doudna and Emmanuelle Charpentier, who set out to answer one question and ended up solving another problem entirely. Doudna and Charpentier were both studying *bacterial* immunity, trying to figure out how bacteria use CRISPR to fight off infections. But as they learned more about how CRISPR worked, they had their own bingo! BIG INDEPENDENT DISCOVERY moment… they realized that CRISPR-Cas9 could be used to repair or edit other kinds of cells too— even *human* and *plant* cells.

Since their discovery, CRISPR-Cas9 has been used to create mushrooms that can last longer on grocery store shelves, to grow more rice on smaller patches of land to feed more people, and to modify mosquitoes so they don't spread life-threatening diseases. It's also being studied to see how it might be used to cure cancers and hereditary diseases and even to develop a treatment or cure for COVID-19. CRISPR's potential is boundless. For their work and their discovery, Doudna and Charpentier were awarded the 2020 Nobel Prize in Chemistry—the first all-female team to ever receive the award.

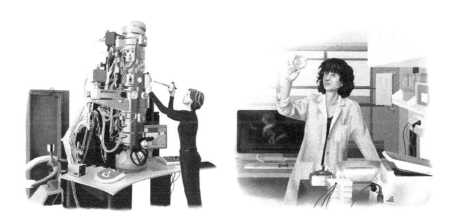

*Nobel Prize winning scientists Jennifer Doudna and
Emmanuelle Charpentier*

Doudna and Charpentier are like Spiderwoman and Tigra or Batgirl and Black Canary, a fearless superduo working together to make the world a better place. But sometimes superheroes have to find their strength on their own. Now, you may not have heard of CRISPR before, but I'm fairly certain you've heard of COVID-19. Let me tell you about a superhero behind one of the most effective COVID-19 vaccines available today. This particular superhero grew up in Hungary, the daughter of a butcher. As a young girl she never had the opportunity to meet a scientist, but she still dreamed of becoming one. Eventually, through hard work and dedication to her studies, our superhero—Katalin Karikó—succeeded.

Sometimes superheroes have to find their strength on their own.

Early in her scientific career, Karikó discovered the power of mRNA to fight disease. Messenger RNA (or mRNA) is what the body uses to tell its cells which proteins to make—those proteins are what keep us alive and healthy. In theory, you can design mRNA that will tell your cells exactly which types of proteins to make. And if your body makes the right type of proteins, it could defend itself against an invading virus or repair organs or tissue that had been damaged from disease. The potential of designer mRNA enormous.

Karikó could make her mRNA work perfectly on cells in a petri dish. But the problem was that whenever she tried it on mice, it made the mice sick. Their bodies saw the mRNA as a foreign threat, and they attacked it just like they would a virus. Seeing how the mRNA affected mice, most researchers believed the approach could never work in humans and many gave up pursuing research in the field. Karikó understood the scope of the problem but she wasn't yet ready to give up. She was open to the idea that designer mRNA may not work in humans, but she hadn't yet proved that it couldn't, and she wasn't going to give up until she had her answer—no matter what it may be.

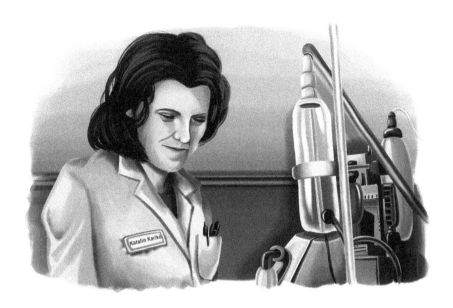

Karikó worked on her experiments hour after hour during the days and then spent her nights writing grants and applying for funding for her work—grants and applications that were almost always rejected. Still, she was focused on finding her answer. She talked over the problem with any scientist prepared to listen and rather incessantly with her colleague and close collaborator Drew Weissman. The main problem in the mouse experiments was that the mRNA caused the mouse's immune system to overreact. So why weren't the immune systems of the mice in the control group overreacting?

The mice in the control group weren't receiving the messenger RNA that was being tested in the other mice, they were receiving *transfer RNA* (or tRNA) instead. It turns out that tRNA has a special molecule inside of it that can help it slip past immune defenses. When you added that molecule to the designer mRNA and then test it out in mice... bingo! BIG INDEPENDENT DISCOVERY—it works!! That discovery and the fundamental research by Karikó, Weissman and their other colleagues working on mRNA inspired a whole new generation of scientists and eventually led to the creation (in record time, mind you!) of the most effective COVID-19 vaccines in distribution today, as I write.

One of those vaccines was developed by another young scientist whose name I hope you file away in a very important place in your mind—you're probably going to be hearing it echoed for a long time to come. Kizzmekia Corbett leads COVID vaccine development for the National Institutes of Health, bumping elbows with Presidents and big name scientists alike.

Kizzmekia Corbett is visited by U.S. President Joe Biden in the midst of the COVID-19 pandemic

She and one of her colleagues, Dr. Barney Graham, designed the basic structure of an mRNA COVID-19 vaccines over one weekend in January 2020, based only on the gene sequence of the virus. And one year later, that vaccine was being rolled out to millions of people around the world.

Corbett grew up in a very (very!) small community in North Carolina, surrounded by tobacco farms and soybean farms. At her elementary school, she was known as the kid who always jumped up to help her classmates out with their work, quick to answer questions about things she knew well and even quicker to ask questions about the things she didn't. In fourth grade, one of her teachers took notice of her and suggested she enroll in more advanced classes. Her parents let her move up in reading and math and by the time she was in high school she was a bonafide whiz kid. By grade ten, she was offered a spot in a special program designed to give high school students who might not normally have the chance the opportunity to study chemistry at the University of North Carolina over the summer.

Once she had her foot in the door, she was off! She could finally see herself in the world of science. And the world of science met her gaze and invited her in. Her hard work and intelligence helped her rise from one lab to another until she was side by side with the President of the United States at the National Institutes of Health. Even though her position in life has grown, her purpose never wavered since childhood. As Corbett described it, "My love for science and solving problems came from my childhood. I was the student who would not leave a math problem unsolved. I won regional science fairs all the way from elementary school and onward. Asking questions about the way the world turns—I like to think of it as somewhat of my purpose in life."

Mighty oaks grow from little acorns.

Mighty oaks grow from little acorns. Remember these stories as you set out on your own. Ask important questions. Devise experiments to find an answer. Then follow the results wherever they may lead. The road won't be easy, far from it. But if your experiments are well crafted and you keep an open mind, you will eventually find an answer… even if it's not the one you were expecting. Sometimes, the answers will be trivial. But if you are lucky, like we were and like the people behind CRISPR and the mRNA vaccines, you may discover something profound, that reshapes humankind for the better.

***

By the end of that first year, my lab was brimming with energetic postdoctoral fellows and a few graduate students, all working on retroviruses. Our research was supported with grants from the National Cancer Institute, the American Cancer Society and the Leukemia Society of America (later renamed the Leukemia & Lymphoma Society.) It was a good time to take the next step, and that required a chat with the president. Emil Frei (everyone called him Tom; you might remember Jack Strominger mentioning him to me, telling me I'd love him) had been the Cancer Institute's president since the death of founder Sidney Farber, and physician-in-chief since Farber recruited him for that role in 1972.

Calm and approachable in his owlish glasses, Tom was one of the most distinguished cancer specialists in the country. He and a former colleague at the National Cancer Institute developed the first cures for childhood leukemia. They called their novel approach combination chemotherapy (which showed that a combination of drugs could be more effective in treating cancer than just one.)

"Tom," I asked, "how can I to apply molecular biology to improve cancer medicine?"

"Bill, the first thing you need to know is *what we don't know*. That will be your jumping off point," he said. "I can't tell you what you will find, but I can tell you where to look. The best way to learn about what we know and don't know is to attend morning rounds," he continued. "We are a teaching hospital. We analyze what is best for each patient one by one. That is how our doctors learn to treat patients. I will ask our attending physicians to introduce you as an observer."

If the snow wasn't too deep or the roads too icy, I would ride my bike the five miles from my Cambridge home to the hospital in Boston. (I can still feel the winter chills seeping through my not-warm-enough jacket and into my bones.) Usually, I joined pediatric rounds starting at 6:30 a.m. Each child's chart was reviewed, then the physician opened discussion for best treatment options.

Whenever I could over the course of two years, I attended the daily sessions of these disciplined, compassionate medical teams. These were some of the most inspiring experiences of my life. I was witness to the very best of what one group of highly educated, dedicated people can do for a fellow human in serious trouble. As the cancer medical teams puzzled out what to do next, patient by patient, I listened as closely as I could to learn what they knew, what they didn't know, and what they needed to know.

A key to discovery is to map the limits of the relevant unknown.

A key to discovery is to map the limits of the relevant unknown. That was my role during these hours as a medical scientist working on behalf of the pediatric cancer team. All too often we assume that we know more than we actually do, or, perhaps even more dangerous, we assume that what we know is *true*. Science leaps into the darkness, the very edge of human knowledge. That is where we begin. Doing cutting edge research is like being in a deep cave facing a wall of hard stone. You do not know what is behind the wall, but you know some truth is there. Your job is to chip away at that rock, not knowing what you are going to find on the other side. It is extremely difficult to explain *how* unknown the unknown is. Some people chip away for a lifetime only to have a pile of flakes at their feet.

Young doctors on morning rounds sought information from me, too. They'd ask me: "How do the drugs we use to treat these children really work? Can we combine them in new ways?" Meantime, I was teaching a course called *Cancer and Society*, and my students—most memorably, two intelligent sophomores named Alan D'Andrea (who became a respected and award-wining cancer researcher) and Christina Lindan (who became a doctor and expert in epidemiology)—were asking about how advances in molecular biology and DNA discoveries could lead to curing disease, namely cancer. So many of us were seeking answers, and the opportunity to heal.

Science leaps into the darkness, the very edge of human knowledge.

Soon, I heard about a new discovery in DNA research that only a few scientists knew about. Good thing I was one of those scientists! Wally Gilbert was about to publish a major paper with a colleague, Allan Maxam, describing a profound method of DNA sequencing. Their method was to treat DNA with chemicals that attach to specific nucleotides. Wally had been tinkering with such chemicals during my last months as a graduate student a few years before. I remembered that many of those chemicals resembled drugs used to treat cancer. The framework for a molecular biochemistry experiment quickly took shape in my mind. The experiment could engage Christina and Alan immediately and, if successful, might provide some answers for the morning rounds physicians.

I envisioned a way to study and determine the cellular biology of how DNA molecules in certain chemicals combat cancer cells. Then, we'd be able to identify pieces of the chemical DNA, as targets to reveal how these anticancer drugs worked! I invited Alan and Christina to my lab. "I have an idea that just might work," I told them.

Sure enough, it did. The very first time Alan ran the tests, *the very first time*, the process worked. "This is unbelievable, Alan!" I exclaimed. "You have shown where the DNA is damaged in cancer cells." Remember: Alan was barely twenty years old, if that! In a short time, we were able to identify the molecular impact of many classic drugs on cancer cells, and even for some newer cancer drugs. Treating defined sequences of DNA with several anticancer drugs allowed us to understand exactly how they worked. In addition, our work supported the idea behind combination therapy: sometimes a combination of drugs works better than a single drug to fight disease. Time for more cookies and cocktails, but first: the rush to publish our results.

I took the results to Tom Frei. "Bill, this is terrific," he said. Here was evidence that combining the right drugs will have a greater effect on treating the cancer, without damaging normal tissues. The effect on cancer is **synergistic**; the effect on normal cells is additive. "We will test these combinations in patients as soon as we can," Tom added, elated.

He decided to test the approach first in patients with head and neck cancer, which is often hard to treat. Tom convinced a cancer surgeon he knew to reverse the normal order of treatment; instead of surgery first and chemotherapy later, chemotherapy would be completed before surgery. The idea was that the new combinations of drugs might radically reduce the size of the tumor, making surgery easier. It was unbelievable to see this practical application of our lab experiments.

Chemotherapy trials, however, take loads of time, typically several years. We needed *ten years* to complete these trials, treating head and neck cancer patients with combinations of cancer drugs, tracking outcomes, some positive, some worrying. Every human body is different and so are their illnesses; this is why we needed so much time to test and analyze the results. But in the end, this change in treatment proved worth the wait. The new approach increased the survival rate for head and neck cancer patients from twenty percent to eighty percent! To me, that is science at its best… making a difference, a *big* difference, to people's lives.

***

Tom quickly understood the power of applying the latest advances in biochemistry to understanding how cancer drugs work. One day, Tom turned to me and said, "Bill, why don't you create a new division to grow our own cancer **pharmacologists**? We can make a real difference to improving cancer care around the country."

I was only an assistant professor at that point—still sporting jeans most of the time and still using a bicycle as my primary form of transportation. So I was truly surprised. Yet here he was, the president of the Dana-Farber Cancer Institute suggesting that I become the equivalent of a department chairman.

"I'd very much like to do it!" I said. But then I paused a moment—as you now know me to do when someone I highly respect offers me an exciting new career opportunity. I continued, "I have a few questions." (Subtext: even when presented with what appears to be your favorite sweet treat, make sure to read the ingredients.)

"Fire away," he said.

"I want continue my work with viruses. Is that okay?"

"Sure," he said. "You can do any research you want. You will be your own boss."

"Great." (Subtext: YESSS!) "But who will we train?," I asked, "and how do you imagine that will work? Who will pay for the training?"

"Simple," he said. He then was so explicit about what he had in mind for creating a department specifically for research on anticancer drugs that it was apparent he'd been thinking about this for some time. Not so simple, actually, but conceived with Tom's rare administrative talent of vision and precision.

He then told me that I could hire five or six junior professors, all of whom would have salary and research assistance. He said that each year, the institute accepts new clinical fellows (I would be in charge of selecting one or two of them) who will join for a period of five to seven years to become specialists in cancer treatment. A supergroup, so to speak. Training grants will cover costs, and patient care would be everyone's primary focus.

I loved the idea, just loved it. It fit my goal of applying science to the practical issues of treating patients.

I served as chair of what we called the Division of Biochemical Pharmacology for the next seven years. During that time, I continued my work on both viruses and DNA damage. Research findings from my laboratory and the pharmacology division significantly advanced the understanding of a wide range of anticancer drugs—drugs that remain the mainstay of most cancer treatment regimes today. The biochemical pharmacology division grew to include five outstanding faculty members. Many fellows became assistant professors. Several are now highly regarded physician scientists leading departments of cancer pharmacology. Just as Tom Frei imagined. Another golden example of why it's important to listen to your mentors; they usually have wonderful ideas. And sometimes, through their ideas, you can save a human live (or many human lives!). If that's not the stuff of superpowers, I'm not sure what is.

CHAPTER 7

Fighting Aids and Aiding the Fight

By 1980 (think scrunchies and The Rubik's Cube), our DNA research on anticancer drugs was thriving. At our lab, we were among a small group of scientists still on the hunt to prove that viruses can cause cancer in humans. There was enough research out there—though largely ignored—which showed that a retrovirus could lie sleeping in a host (a cow, in this case) and then wake up suddenly to cause cancer in the animal. Those studies and our knowledge of how viruses infect cells and replicate led me to think we were on the right track.

"These viral cancer infections probably attack humans the same way they attack cattle," I thought.

Then, in the spring of 1981 (think the launch of MTV and the birth of Justin Timberlake) came the unforgettable call from a scientist named Bob Gallo. Bob had been working to isolate human retroviruses. He was overjoyed. "Bill, we did it! We discovered a human retrovirus that causes leukemia!"

"Fantastic! Congratulations!" I said. For all of us who believed that viruses could cause cancer, Bob's message was a magical moment. We knew immediately that this discovery would open doors to new research on cancer viruses that would turn into millions of lives saved.

I asked Bob for more details. He told me it was an entirely new form of leukemia he'd detected, one which he suspected was transmitted sexually, or from mother to child. He called it HTLV (the Human T cell Leukemia Virus).

We knew immediately that this discovery would open doors to new research on cancer viruses that would turn into millions of lives saved.

That call started me on one of the most exciting—and important—scientific adventures of my life. The virus Bob described reminded me of a mouse virus I was studying with a postdoctoral fellow, Joseph Sodroski (now a prize-winning expert in just about every kind of "ology"—virology, microbiology, immunology...the list goes on). Joe and I had ideas to explore, and Bob was on board for exploring, too. After closely studying DNA copies of the HTLV (and another very similar one found shortly after, named HTLV-1), we discovered that HTLV was different from all other known retroviruses in that it *activated itself.* We called this *transactivation.* I immediately suspected that transactivation was also the answer to how the virus caused leukemia. I thought, "If the virus could change the cell to favor itself, maybe it could also change the cell to favor *the growth* of those cells."

For the next two years, we tested this hypothesis. You know when you scratch the surface of a big topic and then you can't stop scratching? You want to know *everything* there possibly is to know. That is how I felt about HTLV. I *needed to* learn as much as I could about the natural history of HTLV—how it was passed from person to person and how it spread in large groups of people.

"The best way to understand this virus is to go where Bob first located it, and where it causes the most trouble— Japan," I reasoned. "If I really understand how HTLV behaves, I will know where and how to look for the *next* human retroviruses."

All right, then, off I went with my family to Japan! Working with Japanese scientists as a visiting professor at the University of Kyoto, I learned that HTLV is transmitted from mother to child through breast milk and by exposure to vaginal fluids during childbirth. Infections can also transmitted by blood transfusions and by sex. It isn't the virus alone that infects someone, but rather a virus-infected cell. Cell-to-cell spread is a very unusual mode of virus transmission.

I also learned why it was so hard to find human retroviruses; the disease occurs only *many years* after infection, just like what we saw in cattle and other large animals. For HTLV, the period between infection and disease is quite long, typically 20-40 years. Even then only about five percent of those infected fall ill. During the long quiet period very little virus appears in the blood, if any. With no virus in the blood, and absent disease, it is difficult if not impossible to find a new virus.

Our studies of HTLV were exciting and important on their own. But they soon became even more important to the world, because it helped us understand another rare human retrovirus—unknown to us at the time but silently spreading and on its way to becoming a pandemic. This new disease is one that I'm guessing you've heard about, AIDS (Acquired Immune Deficiency Syndrome). Once I and my fellow scientists understood the deadly threat of this new disease, it was our duty to devote our minds and efforts to learning about the disease and hopefully finding a cure.

***

I remember, it was a cold, dark December day (good things don't usually happen on cold, dark December days, except maybe on Christmas and during Hanukkah). On this particular day, I came across a paper in *The New England Journal of Medicine*. Michael Gottlieb, a young immunologist, and several other doctors at UCLA Medical School described a new illness that they thought might be spreading—a new type of cancer, they suspected. During the previous year Michael had seen a number of young men with the same scary symptoms—their white blood cells were depleted and their immune systems were breaking down.

I couldn't stop thinking about that paper. Over Christmas break, I kept re-reading it. I was worried. And with worry came my deep motivation to help.

Once I and my fellow scientists understood the deadly threat of this new disease, it was our duty to devote our minds and efforts to learning about the disease and hopefully finding a cure.

I knew that retroviruses could attack the immune system. "Maybe a retrovirus like HTLV *causes* this disease," I thought, noting how it seemed to be similar to HTLV, targeting the same kind of cells and transmitted from one person to another, maybe by sex. I had read that the UCLA scientists hadn't found a new virus, but to me, that didn't mean much. As we saw, viruses like HTLV go silent for a long time after the initial infection. So what did I do? I called on the superheroes and their superbrains. Of course this included Bob Gallo, who said he was thinking along the same lines. "It sure looks like a variant of HTLV to me," he said.

At Bob's suggestion, we put together a small working group to collect as much information as we could about this new disease. We met every few weeks along with a rotating cast of experts in other fields. Based on our research, we quickly narrowed in on the idea that this new disease was caused by a retrovirus and nothing else.

Around the same time, there was another scientist in the United States who was just as concerned about the spread of this new disease as we were, someone you're probably very familiar with. His name? Dr. Anthony Fauci. Tony was a senior investigator with the National Institute of Allergy and Infectious Diseases at the time, an institution he went on to become director of just a few years later. He too had assembled a team of superhero scientists to study the disease, meeting with patients at the clinical center he ran. That's how science works—all of us working together, but separately, to solve the same problem. He in his lab, and I in mine, we were all trying to figure out what was causing this illness.

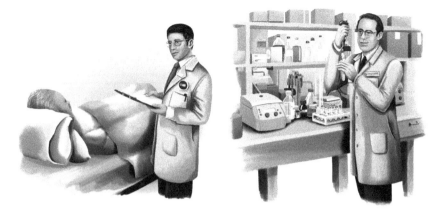

Anthony Fauci and I, working separately in our own labs to solve the same problem.

In our lab, we had a core group investigating what we called "the retrovirus theory of AIDS", which included Jim Curran of the Centers for Disease Control and leading scientists from Germany, England and France. Data began to pour in from other sources. Donna Mildvan— an incredible infectious disease specialist at Mt. Sinai Hospital in New York City—noticed that some drug users were dying of a new degenerative brain disease that might be similar to the one we were studying. To test for the presence of a new virus Donna sent brain tissue from autopsies of these drug users to primate centers for testing in chimpanzees. Had the disease appeared quickly in chimps, Donna would have been first to find the virus. Instead, it took many years before her chimps became ill. Sometimes doing the right experiment doesn't lead to the right answer quickly.

Meanwhile, cities worldwide were seeing an increasing number of individuals—mostly men—with the same symptoms initially reported in Gottleib's paper. Then, an entirely different population of patients appeared: infants born to mothers with the disease and recipients of blood transfusions. This widening circle of infection reinforced our retrovirus theory—the virus was being passed on in the same way as HTLV.

With all known virus and other microorganisms ruled out as the cause of AIDS, the hunt for a new virus gained speed. Another pressing question on the research front: Did people with AIDS have antibodies to the virus? New tests soon gave us the answer. Yes. *All people with AIDS had antibodies to the new virus.* We had discovered the cause of AIDS, a new type of retrovirus. A committee eventually gave the virus a consensus name: HIV (Human Immunodeficiency Virus).

The ability to test people for HIV infection unleashed another bombshell. Many, many more people were infected with the virus both in the United States and worldwide than actually had AIDS. Not yet. Knowing these viruses as I did, I was afraid of what was coming. Many, if not most, of those infected might develop AIDS over time and die. The epidemic had already spread further than anybody had imagined. The disease we knew as AIDS was only the tip of a very large iceberg of infection.

By 1984, AIDS was nearly always fatal and it was spiraling out of control. I feared this disease would become a global pandemic with potential to kill hundreds of millions. AIDS had to be cured, and I was determined to play a role. The threat to global public health was so urgent, and my skills in medical science so well-matched against the threat, I knew I had to shift gears at Dana-Farber and make combating AIDS my highest priority. No longer was I the curious-but-helpless child on the periphery of the polio outbreak; no, now I was in the thick of another disease-ridden chapter of history, this time with the tools and skills to make a difference.

I feared this disease would become a global pandemic with potential to kill hundreds of millions. AIDS had to be cured, and I was determined to play a role.

"Now is the time to apply everything you know...," I pep-talked myself. "Use your knowledge of science and medicine to understand the virus and to discover drugs to stop the virus. Do what you can to gain more research dollars to recruit the talent we need. Use your knowledge of the biotechnology pharmaceutical industry to engage their capacity. Use your antiwar experience to raise awareness of the peril and to mobilize public opinion and research support…Do this all at the same time. It will be a challenge of a lifetime."

Note: By 2020, while the global AIDS cumulative death toll would exceed thirty-two million people, the number of people living with AIDS infection was higher, at thirty-eight million and, of those, twenty-five million were receiving antiretroviral treatments. Without the work of the scientific and medical communities, the toll would have been much greater.

***

The first challenge was a big one, one which has been with us all since birth: fear. The fear among many fellow scientists and physicians at Dana-Farber was that working closely with the virus would endanger them and their patients. "Why bring a new and deadly virus, one that causes a disease with no cure, into our hospital?" several protested. Some were so hostile they thought I should be fired.

Baruj Benacerraf, the Nobel Prize winning immunologist who had recently succeeded Tom Frei as the institute's president, had a courageous answer.

"As medical scientists dedicated to using our knowledge to fight disease we have an obligation to do what we can. I will personally take the responsibility," he asserted, "to assure our work on this disease will not endanger our patients or our staff."

Baruj (a Hebrew name, pronounced bah-ROOK) gave me the green light to accelerate HIV related research and create a formal new research unit, the Division of Human Retrovirology. An entire department dedicated to retrovirology was the first of its kind in the world. Over the next few years, I recruited an excellent faculty; many were my former graduate students and postdoctoral fellows. By the end of the decade, we would number more than one hundred. Strength in numbers if I ever did see it.

Soon, we were able to determine that HIV, in terms of growth and infection, did behave similarly to HTLV. We were able to determine the virus' DNA sequence and study its working parts. We found new proteins (unknown to science at the time) in the core of the virus genome; learning more about these proteins could help us fight the virus. How? Well, I knew that we needed to find new drugs that stopped the virus from growing if we were to treat and hopefully someday cure people infected by HIV. To do that we needed to discover which proteins the virus needed to reproduce itself.

"Here is what we are going to do next," I said to my team. "We are going to introduce changes (mutations) all along the virus genome and see what happens. We are looking for changes that kill the virus. If any knock out the ability of the virus to make a protein then we know that protein will be a good target for an antiviral drug. Let's get to work."

And work we did. We eventually found a chink in the virus armor; if we could inactivate a certain gene, we could find a way to kill the virus. Go, go, go!

My colleague, Roberto Patarca, and I exploring the virus' genome and looking for chinks in its armor.

***

I called my team together to focus on the next step in fighting the new disease: transforming discovery to treatment and cures.

"Our mission is to use our knowledge to stop the pandemic. We can do it," I said with great optimism, however cautious. "We *need* to develop drugs to stop HIV/AIDS. We know better than anyone how to do so. We know the virus weak spots." Of course this feat couldn't be achieved by us alone. "We will be working in partnership with biotech and Big Pharma companies," I continued. "They have resources we can't match. But we can point the way and deliver the materials they need. Our job is to make their job easier."

For the next three years, well into 1987, our lab set out to do exactly that.

Meanwhile, the death toll from AIDS was climbing terribly. So what did I do? I went on a crusade to find new partners to deliver new drugs to treat AIDS patients. I began knocking on the doors of CEOs and research directors at major pharmaceutical companies and deans and presidents of elite research institutes. My passion and purpose were aflame, but often in the world of scientific innovation, this can only take you so far; support is needed— financial and otherwise.

I was granted meetings, but no funds. Everywhere, the same story. "Sorry Bill. Funds for research are already fully budgeted for this year. No way we could start a new program now." Some added, "Besides, there are many diseases much more important than AIDS." I wanted to scream.

My passion and purpose were aflame, but often in the world of scientific innovation, this can only take you so far; support is needed— financial and otherwise.

I kept pushing the pharmaceutical companies, arguing that they should develop new drugs against diverse targets. My experience with Dana-Farber cancer treatments and the vision I shared with Tom Frei reinforced my beliefs about the importance of combination drug therapy. Cancer cells are sneaky; they are master escape artists. Give them one drug and they will find a way to survive. Give them two, you might have a chance. Hit them with three, now we're talking— you had a good chance of winning.

The response in universities and research institutes was practically the same as Big Pharma's. And even more frustrating, because I expected more from them. Renowned scientists leading infectious disease and microbiology departments voiced appreciation for our detective work to locate molecular vulnerabilities in HIV. But, in effect, they said their hands were tied.

*****

Meanwhile, there had been no progress in the development of an HIV vaccine. Though HIV produced large concentrations of antibodies for infected individuals, those antibodies did not stop the virus from growing. It was becoming clear that once infected, AIDS patients were infected with HIV for life. Drugs could be developed, and so much knowledge would be gained on the immune system as well as the virus itself, but a vaccine was not looking possible. At the time—1986 and still in the throes of this battle— I concluded that it might take twenty-five to thirty years before developing a vaccine; it was crushing to deliver this estimate to sufferers of the illness, and their families. It's with heavy heart that as I write to you now, thirty-five years later, there is still no HIV vaccine. (But we should never say never…)

At that time, my worry was growing heavier and heavier. Remember my anxiety rock? Well this was a boulder. With no vaccine, there would be a tidal wave of human loss, unless we could develop drugs to treat infected patients and block HIV growth. HIV had remained my first priority in Dana-Farber research, but it was not all consuming. My cancer pharmacology lab continued to make big strides in identifying combinations of drugs to treat cancer—just as Tom Frei and I had envisioned.

"Maybe a combination of antiviral drugs will work against HIV," I kept thinking. "We learned from cancer that one drug is not enough, but cancer cells have a much harder time escaping when two or more drugs are combined to attack different targets in the cancer." I briefed our team on the reasoning, and added an additional thought. "If the drugs work to stop the virus in an infected person, maybe they can also prevent a person from being infected in the first place." This very questioning—and the ensuing discoveries Joe Sodroski and I made on hybrid viruses—became the backbone for many HIV vaccine research programs ongoing now in the US and worldwide.

Good news arrived in 1986 when the FDA (Food and Drug Administration) announced and approved the first anti-HIV drug, known as azidothymidine (AZT). Work on AZT had started decades before, long before HIV was ever even known to exist. Two scientists, Gertrude Elion and George Hitchings, had been working together to explore how nucleic acids (DNA and RNA) were metabolized in different types of cells. Their hope was that in understanding the differences they could develop drugs that would block the synthesis of nucleic acids in cancer cells, but leave normal cells alone—a cure for cancer! Over their years working together, they developed a whole library of new drugs that could treat a whole variety of diseases, from leukeumia to malaria, even the gout. But many of the compounds they developed didn't do much beyond the petri dishes and mice in which they were tested. At least, nothing that seemed immediately applicable...until HIV, that is.

Gertrude Elion and George Hitchings

Much like the rest of us in the scientific community, Elion and Hitchings were equally worried about the spread of AIDS. The more they read, the more they realized that one of the drugs they had worked in the 1960s might prove useful against HIV, a compound that had been able to stop a mouse retrovirus from replicating—you'll remember HIV was a retrovirus as well. They sent the drug to a researcher and friend at the National Institutes of Health, Samuel Broder, suggesting he test it against HIV. You've probably figured it out already, but that drug was AZT, and when Broder tested the compound against the new virus...it worked! We had our first successful treatment for the disease. (Elion and Hitchings were later awarded the Nobel Prize for their work on this drug and the many others they developed together over the years in their lab.) But unfortunately for all of us and especially for those still suffering from AIDS, the joy was short-lived. It turned out that most AIDS patients developed resistance to the drug within six months to a year.

This development was concerning, but not unexpected. You probably expected as much too, right? Because HIV, as we'd learned, is a master at escape. So, we urgently needed to find a new anti-HIV drug to *pair* with AZT in order to foil this elusive HIV response. Again, this need for combination therapy rose to the forefront of my thoughts. This is what would stop HIV (just as we had accelerated its impact against cancer in our Dana-Farber Division of Biochemical Pharmacology).

In time, I became known among AIDS activists, HIV researchers and news reporters as "Dr. Combination." A cool nickname, but not as cool as this: we finally landed on an effective drug combination, and many who received that combo in the early 1990s are alive and well today. Now, the great majority of HIV positive people receiving combination drug therapy can expect to live a near normal life.

You probably won't be surprised to know that the research didn't stop there. In the world of science, research is a constant. We can *always* learn more. So, still determined to best understand how the virus attacks cells, we turned our attention to antibodies. We thought (and hoped): if we could trick the body into making a highly specialized class of antibodies we knew resided on the cell surface, maybe we could stop the infection before it starts. I learned about this category of antibodies while mining through everything I could read about mucosal immunology—the study of the immune responses that happen at mucosal membranes of the intestines and other parts of the body. And indeed, one particle of a certain size stimulated mucosal immunity.

I was so optimistic about this idea that I cofounded a company—Virus Research Institute—to research and develop these antibodies with Robert Langer. Robert already was a world expert on bio-particles; today he is a legendary MIT professor, scientist and inventor best known for ingeniously applying nanoscience through novel materials to improve human health and medicine.

The company was a success but my idea to stimulate immunity in mucosa? Not so much. Our experiments demonstrated to our initial excitement that antibodies *could* block HIV infection of T cells, but we were deeply disappointed when we found that the antibodies had no effect on other cells infected with HIV. I felt deflated but determined to press on; no, it was more than determination. It was necessity. It was my purpose.

I felt deflated but determined to press on; no, it was more than determination. It was necessity. It was my purpose.

***

The public's understanding about AIDS was abysmal; many people were uninformed—or misinformed—about how the disease was transmitted (primarily through unprotected sex, between all genders though early cases were predominantly detected in males), and as a result, people weren't changing how they behaved. Awareness was limited, cases went unreported, and lives were being lost. There was a healthy dose of denial here in the United States; scientists and policy makers had tracked the course of the pandemic in other countries, and many of us knew what was inevitably coming our way, especially if the public didn't have the information to protect themselves.

I remember thinking, "If what is happening in Africa happens here in the U.S. we are looking at twelve million Americans dying of AIDS. Even half that number is horrible to contemplate."

After talking with the leading epidemiologists, doctors, and medical scientists of the time, I asked myself, "What is my responsibility in the face of a pending disaster of such magnitude?" The range of potential activities could have been dizzying. Okay, fine, they *were* dizzying. But I had to keep my head on. So, this is how I broke it down, a focused four-prong agenda for action:

- **Mobilize medical and science community**. Bring all the superheroes together and make sure everyone is suited up, all hands on deck, all superpowers switched to "on" position. Also: petition the government for funding. Money is crucial to research the disease, to recruit scientists to join the fray, to design and develop drugs, and last but absolutely not least, to provide social services for those infected.

- **Engage civil society**. Create nonprofit organizations to raise money and convince the government to do more.

- **Speak out**. Public forums, media interviews, private receptions, meetings with activist groups, wrangle your contacts and make phone calls and pleas to influential figures. Use your voice, raise your voice, alert the public to the danger ahead and what they can do to protect themselves and their families.

- **Destigmatize the disease**. Educate the public on the nature of the illness, strike down prejudice, dispel false theories about who can fall ill, let people know the risks, the precautions.

Ready, set, deep breath, *go.*

***

The first nonprofit group created to confront the epidemic, the AIDS Medical Foundation, was organized in 1983 in New York City. Its leaders were Joseph Sonnebend, an infectious disease specialist, and Mathilde Krim, a geneticist and immunologist with a long history of supporting cancer research and social causes. When we met, Mathilde was in the early stages of joining forces with the California based National AIDS Research Foundation, established by the famous actress Elizabeth Taylor and Michael Gottlieb, the first doctor to describe AIDS in 1981. Their merged organizations officially became the American Foundation for AIDS Research (amfAR) later in 1985.

Mathilde and I hit it off immediately. She agreed with my priorities and asked me to join their board. "We'll need a scientific advisory committee," she said, "Are you willing to be the chair and recruit like-minded scientists and doctors?"

Absolutely. I was delighted to find in Mathilde someone with social and political connections who saw the disease threat as I did. For the next five years I worked closely with amfAR shuttling back and forth between our meetings in Los Angeles and New York as we established ourselves as the leading nonprofit anti-AIDS foundation. amfAR's close connection with Hollywood was an enormous help. When I mentioned making pleas for funds to influential figures, I didn't know that I'd be making many of these pleas with the humongously famous movie star Elizabeth Taylor!

Elizabeth Taylor, in fact, became the most famous advocate for AIDS victims, raising hundreds of millions of dollars for research. She was one of the most passionate, articulate and effective public figures to warn of AIDS' dangers. Close friends of hers and even a family member were already infected. And of course, she was aware that Rock Hudson, another big star and dear friend of hers, was seriously ill.

Elizabeth was warm, radiant, well-educated and fun to be around. And most importantly: *people listened to her*, which was just what we needed to push awareness of the AIDS crisis into the mainstream, turn public opinion and promote private funding for a cure. When I asked her to help me convince leaders in Congress to approve a huge increase in taxpayer funding for AIDS research, she said immediately:

"You tell me where and when and I'll be there."

I wanted to use whatever money we raised to rapidly fund research and recruit talented scientists. A few singer-songwriters in the group, such as Barry Manilow and Carol Bayer Sager, were not so sure. "Our friends need help," they pleaded. "We should give *them* the money to live, or at least to make their last days more pleasant."

Like other celebrities on the board, David Geffen (American music business mogul, philanthropist, and film producer) counted many personal friends suffering from AIDS. He had deep ties in the entertainment industry as founder and head of Geffen Records and a former top talent manager at the William Morris Agency. Yet David also was passionate about stopping the epidemic.

"I understand the need to help those with AIDS," he said. "However, if we don't find a way to stop the disease, we will only end up having more and more people to support. We need science to stop the epidemic. I vote for Bill's proposal."

David was persuasive. His argument clinched the issue, setting the policy for what is now thirty-five years of amfAR research grants. I could not have done it without him. Many of our country's leading HIV/AIDS scientists today got their start from those early amfAR grants.

***

The next few years were intense, busy, satisfying, and still scary, as the virus raged on. Thankfully though, almost every day we were learning more about how HIV caused the disease, where we might attack the virus with drugs and other strategies to stop it. Again: we weren't alone. With new money pouring in from Congress and private donors, scientists all over the United States were eager to fight the fight. I crisscrossed the country speaking at universities and research institutes, responding to requests to explain what we knew about HIV and help jump-start new research projects.

For a time I was one of the few scientists willing to talk about HIV and AIDS to reporters. News of Rock Hudson's illness and rapid decline before his death in early October 1985 shook the nation, jolting people everywhere to ask themselves, Am I at risk? Are my children at risk? Will the disease be confined to a few risk groups: homosexuals, drug users, blood transfusion recipients? Is AIDS transmitted by casual contact, touching, sneezing, kissing? It was our duty as medical scientists to answer these questions.

The AIDS story, long shunned by editors and news directors of mainstream media, now was featured on the covers of *Time* and *Newsweek* and the front page of *USA*

Today. AIDS segments increasingly were "next up," a topic for morning programs with millions of viewers, ABC's *Good Morning America* and NBC's *Today*, as well as network evening news programs anchored by Peter Jennings and Tom Brokaw. I was interviewed by them all. Now was not the time to be camera shy. (I could not have anticipated, of course, that I again would be recruited as a pandemic expert on TV when COVID-19 fears surged in 2020, or that those interviews would happen across a strange and not-yet-invented internet platform called Zoom.)

Across the pond, in England, another radiant, extraordinarily popular celebrity whose star power might have matched Elizabeth Taylor's, committed her fame and courage to the cause: Princess Diana. I'd been pushing for this to happen, trying to reach her through some connections. "It will make a difference not just in England but around the world," I argued. "People everywhere look up to British royalty." And it was true. When Princess Diana did visit an AIDS ward, the pictures were stunning and made an enormous, immediate impact. Princess Diana shaking hands with men, weakened and visibly ill, some in wheelchairs. Princess Diana holding and hugging babies with AIDS, their tiny fingers wrapped around one of hers. The images drew extraordinary coverage on front pages and newscasts around the world.

For the next eight years, until her tragic death, Princess Diana did more than anyone else to soften the public's perception of people with AIDS. Moreover, I am convinced that those images from the very outset did more to de-stigmatize AIDS than all government campaigns and pronouncements combined. Never again did reporters ask me, "Can I catch AIDS by being around sick people?"

Also during those years, the fashion world was particularly devastated, with hundreds of high-profile designers, models and executives succumbing to AIDS. Several leading designers reached out to me with urgent requests. Could I advise them, for example, on how to help de-stigmatize HIV/AIDS in their own country? Yes, of course.

I worked with designer Valentino and his partner on gala events in Italy. The centerpiece, a major news story in Italy, was an award presented to Elizabeth Taylor one night at the international conference on HIV/AIDS in Florence, where I had the honor of introducing her. "People living with AIDS need our love and support," she said in her acceptance remarks. "Please, please help them." Karl Lagerfeld and Chanel followed the same script in Paris; this time with awards to Catherine Deneuve and other celebrated French actors. (If you're not familiar with Catherine Deneuve, I suggest you watch her in the very magical/very weird movie-musicals—*The Umbrellas of Cherbourg* and *Donkey Skin*—after you finish this chapter. They're oldies...and in French...but worth your time and eyeballs, I promise.)

Easily the best experience for me among many AIDS-related events and campaigns was collaborating with Niki de Saint Phalle, a fabulous French-American sculptor, painter and filmmaker. Niki put all her talent and energy into a book to help teenagers and children understand AIDS. Translated into German, Italian and Japanese, the book highlighted what was and was not risky behavior. *AIDS: You Can't Catch It Holding Hands*, an illustrated letter to her son Philip, was an arresting, creative way to educate and inform thousands of young people about the dangers of unprotected sex and needle sharing by intravenous drug use. With great pride, I helped her with some scientific facts and soon we became great friends. In all, seventy thousand books were distributed free in schools. A 1988 *People* magazine article quoted me, quite accurately: "This book is crucial." And so was Niki.

***

Many of the celebrities I mention so far in this chapter may not be as well known today as they were then. But do you know who is an even bigger star today than they were in the 1980s? The scientist! Dr. Tony Fauci.

First, a little background. From the early '80s as AIDS infections began to soar, activists became furious, staging angry protests against the FDA, NIH (National Institutes of Health) and scientific institutes. They demanded access to any experimental drug with a glimmer of potential to slow or cure the disease. In private meetings at the NIH and amfAR, I saw this intensity surge, pushing activists to new extremes in their desperation for any cure. Enter Tony Fauci again, now promoted to head of the National Institute for Allergies and Infectious Disease and one our strongest allies in government for accelerating AIDS research. He recruited me to his grant approving council, an official group that in addition to having final say on which scientists and what research would receive federal funding, also sought or provided advice to people in government, civil and scientific communities.

I worked with Fauci and the council to bring several top U.S. academic labs and companies (such as Bristol-Myers, Pfizer and Johnson & Johnson) together to work on HIV research and drug development. We also relied on wealthy private donors—more Hollywood actors, producers, and philanthropists included. I'm proud to point out that we succeeded in getting many talented scientists and other individuals thinking about and working on AIDS. I played an essential role in the early response, speeding up the process. This is another example of how one person can make a difference. If you are determined, energetic and have the right vision, you can make a big difference. That difference, if you are lucky, can save hundreds of thousands, even millions of lives. It is a wonderful feeling to know that I was able to do that. But of course, I was not alone.

If you are determined, energetic and have the right vision, you can make a big difference. That difference, if you are lucky, can save hundreds of thousands, even millions of lives.

Far sighted research paid off in the early '80s, and, as millions of people with AIDS living nearly normal lives likely would agree, far sighted research has continued to pay off— not only in continuing breakthroughs in HIV/AIDS research but also in vaccines and treatments to combat the COVID-19 pandemic. It will continue to pay off if we as a country recommit to supporting our best and brightest scientists.

***

"I think your motto should be, 'A Country That Works,'" I told Governor Bill Clinton at a private gathering in Manhattan. His 1992 campaign for the Presidency was gathering speed and that night he was asking us for ideas we thought would appeal to voters. "People are worried about their jobs and government dysfunction," I added. "This phrase addresses both."

"Great idea," the future President replied, his eyes fixed on mine. "I understand you work on AIDS. Any ideas for me on that front?"

"The current president isn't giving AIDS the attention it deserves. Young people know that," I said. "You could say something like 'AIDS is yet another example of how this administration is missing the boat on issues key to the lives of young people. I pledge, if I am the President, to take it seriously and do whatever we can to end the epidemic here and around the world.'"

Two nights later, watching Clinton on the Hollywood set of MTV's *Choose or Lose*, I saw him field questions about inhaling marijuana and whether he wore boxers or briefs (I kid you not! You can look it up! Clinton's reply? "Briefs, mostly."), before going on to address HIV/AIDS, framing his policy ideas with my very words.

Clinton was elected, yet two years into his presidency he struggled then failed in his attempts to reform healthcare.

One day, my associate rushed into my office, wide-eyed. "The White House is on the phone!" A friend and close adviser to Clinton, his former chief of staff, was calling me.

"The President is setting up an advisory group of prominent CEOs, which we are calling the President's Leadership Council, and we'd like to have you as a member," he said. Here once again, Clinton was looking for campaign ideas, this time for what many considered a long shot: his re-election in 1996.

It was not long before I found myself in the White House Map Room for the first of four meetings, each with the same one hour format and a different cast of four participants (except for the President, of course). We brainstormed ideas with him, covering a whole series of issues. He was more than smart; he was brilliant. More than any other human being I have ever met, he understood our country. He had emotional connections to the poorest communities in the South, to the wealthiest businesses in New York and everybody in between. He asked deep questions in these meetings, pressing for information, recommendations.

President Bill Clinton and I in the White House Map Room

When you are a government leader, especially a President or party nominee campaigning for President, so many things are coming at you. The crises of the day, fires that must be seen and put out quickly, along with big priorities for the long term that have to be addressed and managed. Presidents and candidates seeking the White House have to make many judgments based on imperfect information. What decisions do I make today? Which experts and advisers do I listen to? Which data and interpretations are most relevant?

Leaders in government, think tanks, business councils, lobbying associations, non-profits and more came to me as they learned of my prominence in cancer and HIV research, in health and genomics, my extensive knowledge in science and health. "We have this problem." "We have this issue." "What do you think?" Each conversation was an opportunity to put into action two of my highest career priorities: leverage government policy to change people's lives for the better, and improve people's health and further, their access to quality healthcare.

***

Years later, in the early 2000s, the then president, George W. Bush, was determined to help Africa cope with the still raging HIV/AIDS epidemic. Thirty million Africans were infected with the AIDS virus then. (That number is equal to the entire populations of Florida and Georgia combined.) He sent a team of prominent health officials and medical scientists (including yours truly and Famous Fauci), Congress members, top administrators of the NIH and World Health Organization and CEOs of several American pharmaceutical companies to a few countries in Africa; we would visit afflicted areas and meet with trusted people our government could rely on if Congress agreed with President Bush's desire to fund medical programs to turn back the frightening AIDS epidemic in Africa.

In Uganda, we visited a tiny remote village where we came upon a kind of haven, if you can conceive of a desolate haven. When a man died of AIDS, villagers blamed the wife, now viewed as a witch, and, along with all her children, forcibly evicted the family. Stigmatized, where could they go? One answer was enclaves of the abandoned, desolate havens such as this.

An uncle, an aunt, a young child and a woman with three children were living in a mud hut on a small parcel of church land with a small vegetable patch. They were distantly related. AIDS had vanquished other members of the family, except two or three being treated by the health ministry. Once a month, these survivors received a big bag of grain and had to make do with this diet and whatever their garden yielded. Every week, the health ministry dispatched someone by motorcycle to deliver HIV pills. The infected woman told us, "You know, I do this because I want to live long enough so my oldest daughter can take care of the rest of my kids."

This proved to be a defining experience for everyone in our group. Expecting misery and despair, we instead found hope... evidence that a program of AIDS treatment could offer better futures to desperate people. Bush had visited Africa twice in the first years of his presidency. I imagined at that moment that he might have seen something like this as well, and wanted my Congressional companions to be moved in the same way.

***

Soon after President Bush returned from his Africa journeys early in his first term, he called Tony Fauci over to the Oval Office.

"I want a plan for the United States to help Africa with AIDS," Bush said.

Tony was eager and prepared, one would expect nothing less from Tony. He had sounded alarms, directed the flow of government money to research labs (including the retrovirus lab I founded at Dana-Farber) and advised physicians in the U.S. and around the world on AIDS patient care—by then, for two decades. African governments for years had turned to him and his teams for help. A few weeks later, Tony returned to the White House and presented his plan. "I don't like it," Bush said. Tony braced momentarily, then brightened as the President continued. "It is not nearly enough," Bush said. "I want a much bigger plan, an entirely different initiative." The President explained he wanted even more funding. "I want to create a new way to get money directly to people treating AIDS in Africa," he said.

Another few weeks, and Tony returns to the Oval Office. As Tony explained to me, Bush took his ideas and "crafted his own plan, the President's Emergency Plan for Fighting AIDS Relief (PEPFAR). He created that. The plan I gave him was not as big or as bold as he wanted."

From my point of view, this is exactly what American Presidents should do. He saw a problem, used the power of the American government and in doing so probably saved at least ten million lives. What is more, in my view, Tony Fauci continually exhibited qualities of the highest character that represent the best in medicine—a strong scientist, dedicated physician and magnificent public servant. If there is one person in the world who has made the greatest contribution to prevention and treatment of HIV/AIDS, that person is Tony … followed closely by George W. Bush.

HIV/AIDS is the worst scourge of infectious disease ever encountered by any civilization. By the end of 2019, the global death toll from HIV/AIDS was thirty-two million people. In all, seventy-seven million had been infected, with estimates of another one point eight million people being infected each year. Those are big, bad numbers.

But look what has been accomplished. Of thirty-six million people living with the disease, more than twenty million are receiving full treatments and living nearly normal lives. More than a million of these patients live in the U.S. Of those twenty million, more than fifteen million receive these treatments through PEPFAR. Moreover, the American people are helping six million orphans and vulnerable children. I expect many of these children are like those kids we met in that tiny mud hut in Uganda nearly twenty years ago, when PEPFAR was only a plan.

We now have the scientific tools—through testing, treatment and education—to prevent HIV infection or make it nearly impossible for an infected person to transmit the virus to someone else. PEPFAR has been an essential part of this story. Tony Fauci, I and others who have been fighting HIV/AIDS from the start, for nearly forty years, explain and emphasize this fact at every opportunity: We can eliminate the scourge of HIV/AIDS. These resources from the American people bring treatments and methods for prevention to millions more.

***

Now that we've spanned years and populations and presidencies and pandemics, I want to briefly turn inward and backward, to someone we met in the first few pages of this book: my mom. As you know, I would not be alive today if it were not for modern pharmaceuticals, beginning with the penicillin my mother convinced Army doctors to give me when I was an infant.

In fact, I may well have died on nine or ten different occasions. Despite the ailments that unsettled me in my youth, I was pretty healthy during my Berkeley days. My mother's own frightful struggles with terrible illness gave me my purpose when I was young, to cure disease and improve human health, but disease in my own body also was a motivating factor then and, as it turned out, more so ever since.

I became allergic to aspirin when I was twenty-one, a symptom that signaled the onset of nasal polyps and asthma. Once every four or five months, my asthma became so bad I could not walk across a room. I had to be rushed to the hospital for adrenaline shots.

For the next two decades, as I was building my career, I needed a **nasal polypectomy** every six to eight weeks. How does that work? The physician would fix a wire loop over a polyp—and *yank*. For each polyp. That's a lot of yanking. It was like having your eyeballs ripped out through your nose. I had several major operations. Brutal surgery that eroded bones in my nasal passage. Sometimes an eyeball would pop out. Not joking.

It took me years to learn that all that disturbance from nasal polyp surgery made my asthma worse. A physician specialist discovered that each time a polyp was removed, new wounds were created, setting conditions for a new polyp to develop. The cycle repeated. Applying a cortisone cleansing rinse called budesonide, the specialist, Dr. David Kennedy, healed my polyp wounds every week or two for a year. He also used a clever, safer technique to remove polyps that grew inside the nasal cavity. I was one of his first patients for these new treatments. He had my condition under control by the time I was in my mid-forties.

But then: a decade of migraine headaches. Cluster migraine attacks occurred frequently into my mid-fifties. The first time I was treated with **sumatriptan pills** was for a migraine that had lasted *three days*. What a relief! I still get migraines, but now thankfully we have sumatriptan pills.

Most people who know me do not think of me as a cancer survivor, but I am. I contracted head and neck cancer in 2015—those same tough cancers Tom Frei and I treated successfully at Dana-Farber with our targeted chemotherapies. A dose of radiation left me in good shape.

I had to have enormous drive to push through all this. I was never coasting. I was fighting to go to work despite my medical issues, fighting every day. My mother had a poignant way of expressing this attitude for outlasting personal health challenges, a mantra inspired I am sure by her own immense physical and mental struggles. She said, often, "The work of the world is done by people who do not feel well the day they do it."

CHAPTER 8

Down to Business

How can a scientist be a businessperson? How can a professor create a company? How many hats can one head wear? In my experience: many.

Creating a company was never part of my plan when I became a Harvard professor. I had only a dim understanding of how corporations were organized and no understanding of finance. Growing up on a naval base—as well as my antiwar activism years later—alerted me to the dark side of business, profiting from weapons made to kill and destroy. Yet, the years I spent dedicated to anticancer treatment and AIDS research, working closely with pharmaceutical companies, opened my eyes to how business could be a positive force for health, how clinical trials were done, and who paid for them. Though the world of science differs from the world of business, they have striking correlations, too; moreover, in order to enact the greatest possible change for good, they may, in fact, *need* one another.

I've come to think of it like this: science is like dressage, a kind of horseback riding which requires the highest form of precision, training, and finesse. Business, however, is like rassling horses—a sport requiring strength, enthusiasm, and thick skin. Both science and business—dressage and rassling—require an individual who is studied, sturdy, and determined. "I'd like to be this individual," I found myself thinking, as the new age of biotechnology was gathering speed during my years as a professor and medical scientist.

Science is like dressage, a kind of horseback riding which requires the highest form of precision, training, and finesse. Business, however, is like rassling horses— a sport requiring strength, enthusiasm, and thick skin.

As labs were consistently racing to apply the new techniques of recombinant DNA and gene splicing to develop new drugs and vaccines, I realized that these research scientists at universities may be creating a *conceptual* breakthrough, but in order to actually bring these new drugs to patients—in order to save lives—we needed to invite business to the party.

"Companies," I reflected, "are the *practical* part of connecting science to medicine."

A trip I took out west (alas, not for the beach but for collecting mouse leukemia viruses for my investigations of retrovirus-causing cancer in animals) marked the tipping point for me in terms of how I thought about business. In Seattle, San Francisco, and San Diego, I met with all different kinds of scientists; each one was excited about their new biotech companies on the sunny horizon and the ways in which they were funding and speeding along research. Most striking to me was my meeting with a research chemist at the Scripps Research Institute named Richard Lerner who had samples of mouse leukemia to show me. Richard had been studying protein structures, specifically how to accelerate response of antibodies to bolster the immune system against infections. "Look at these results," he told me. "Antibodies to these peptide fragments recognize the whole protein." Peptide fragments are short chains of amino acids that help identify an entire protein. He added, "We don't need to purify proteins anymore!" I understood immediately: using peptide fragments should be a *faster, cheaper* way to make vaccines.

On my return flight, I sipped on tomato juice, noshed on peanuts, and thought about my retrovirus research. *How can I apply this new knowledge? What should I be doing?* My neck began to tingle. I wondered, "Might it be possible to create new vaccines using small peptides rather than entire viruses or virus proteins?" Why wouldn't it be possible, given the results Richard had just shown me? "If so, how would I do it? With what viruses?" I knew how long and expensive it was to develop new drugs, ten years and many tens of millions of dollars. Wouldn't these techniques shorten the time and the expense? I knew pets and livestock suffered serious viral infections. These often were lethal if the animals lived long enough. "Why not test the idea in animals? We won't need to go through the FDA," I thought. It would be a shortcut to demonstrate that a vaccine can prevent retrovirus infections that cause cancer. "I can... create a company to do this!"

I called a Wall Street banker-friend, because who better to call when you know not a lot about finances and want to start a business? I told him about my idea for a new biotech company, and how its work would complement—not compete with—my Harvard research. He connected me with a superhero named Deborah Ferris, who'd been instrumental in getting our old pal Wally Gilbert's company, Biogen, off the ground.

"I love the idea and would love to help," she said, eagerly. "You probably don't know this but my father is a specialist in animal diseases. He works on Plum Island in a lab that was built just offshore to prevent any escaping organism from devastating our livestock industry on land. The search for new vaccines is in my blood."

Deborah and I spent the next few days at my dining room table with too many papers and not enough snacks, outlining the technology to develop animal vaccines and a business plan to develop and sell it. We sketched out the market, the timeline, staff roles and projected costs. I penciled myself in as chair of the board of directors and scientific advisory committee, with Deborah as interim chief financial officer. We named the company Cambridge Bioscience.

Soon (and by soon I mean, after weeks of research, meetings, and shopping for business-y suits and briefcases) we received funding from a NYC firm that specialized in biotech companies and they helped us to find a CEO. All systems go!

But...I did have a worry. There was no precedent for a Harvard assistant professor starting a company. How can a scientist be a businessperson? How can a professor create a company? How many hats can one head wear? Harvard's president had voiced skepticism over professors starting companies. Other faculty across the university grumbled, some with outrage, at the notion that biologists or biochemists might turn discoveries developed at Harvard into a personal fortune. Untoward outcomes from starting this company were conceivable, and vexing. I wondered, "If Nobel Prize winners and other famous professors are getting in trouble and fighting with the university about starting companies, what is going to happen to me? This is big-time politics and I am small fry here. Will starting a business endanger my career? Maybe I'll be accused of having a lack of focus."

How can a scientist be a businessperson? How can a professor create a company? How many hats can one head wear?

After conferring with others and looking into the university laws and policies, however, I came to learn that my foray into businessman-territory was okay, and with good faith I could transfer my knowledge of viruses to a business for commercial development. With Harvard's support, I could breathe easy and keep at it with the company. And if I added outstanding faculty scientists to my venture, it would further strengthen my ability to deflect any trouble within the university— should any develop—and of course deepen my brain trust. I quickly recruited two colleagues: Max Essex, chair of the microbiology department at Harvard's School of Public Health as well as a veterinarian/ microbiologist/ animal virus expert extraordinaire, and Bernie Fields, chair of the department of microbiology and molecular genetics at Harvard Medical School and viral infections expert.

Working together in the company bolstered our desire to work together in our labs, accelerating discoveries. The three of us gained a level of trust that translated very easily. When you start a company, you are able to form remarkably tight associations. You all are working toward the same goal, trying to make a product and make money.

With this, Cambridge Bioscience set off on developing its first product: a synthetic vaccine to protect cats from viral leukemia. Our team's blend of relevant, varied expertise gave us a quick start. Max knew that leukemia in infected cats originated in the cats' inability to defend against the outer shell of the virus. I determined the entire genetic sequence of the virus's outer protein shell, essential for identifying targets for a vaccine biochemical structure.

Our chief scientist, Dante Marciani, a Peruvian scientist who started his career at the National Institutes of Health, worked on something called an adjuvant— a chemical agent that spurs the body's immune response to fight a specific disease with high volumes of antibodies. Adjuvants make vaccines more potent.

"I have an idea," he said one day. "The extract of a soap bark tree is used in traditional medicines in Peru because it stimulates the immune system. If you approve, I have a good source who can provide the extract, then I can purify the active ingredient." We were enthusiastic. "Go ahead!"

In a few months, Dante succeeded. *Voila!,* we had our vaccine. (Today that adjuvant, which we named Quil-A, has been at the forefront of research to create a vaccine to prevent COVID-19 and save both lives and economies.) In less than a year, our tests with cats proved the vaccine to be safe and effective. Our efforts were important for science as well as for saving cats! This was the first effective vaccine to prevent retrovirus infection in any mammal, one that is still used today. See? Science and business, hand in hand. Paw in paw.

After this initial triumph, Cambridge Bioscience faced a lot of uncertainty, financial flux, and some failures, too. While this is to be expected of new companies, we were still disheartened— especially after we developed an effective five-minute test for HIV which we hoped and expected could be sold over the counter to thousands of people, and in time, hundreds of thousands. Unfortunately, the government said no, maintaining that such a test would allow people to hide the fact they were infected; further, the FDA refused to allow any HIV home testing. (Eventually—not until 2012!—the FDA did approve an oral test that would provide results within 20 minutes, similar to a home pregnancy test.)

While the company was facing trouble, our Dana-Farber HIV/AIDS research was becoming more urgent by the day and health professionals were desperate for an effective drug treatment. I'd be back in the suit and tie soon, but at the time, I had to step down from the board and concentrate on fast-moving developments and discoveries in both of my labs, retrovirus and pharmacology. Eventually, Cambridge Bioscience was sold—the good news being that the technology we created for vaccine development and other applications continues to thrive.

***

Far from harming my career, creating Cambridge Bioscience turned out to be a huge advantage. I developed trusting relations with two powerful department chairs. Max Essex invited me to become a member of his department at the School of Public Health. And I became a role model and adviser to other faculty members in starting their companies.

In time, Harvard's governing board and administration embraced the benefits of professors starting companies. While still teaching at the medical school, I was asked to chair a university wide committee that clarified rules governing relationships between professors and the companies they seek to start.

Cue the refrain: *How can a scientist be a businessperson? How can a professor create a company? How many hats can one head wear?* People often asked me these questions after I started Cambridge Bioscience.

My answer was that as a professor of science you have all the skills you need to be a successful entrepreneur. You have to do your science and manage your lab as well or better than anybody else in the world. You have to raise money, and awareness. And you have to communicate what you do so people—grant funding institutes, typically—will know what you have done and be willing to support what you do in the future. Your scientific reputation is not only your superpower; if you decide to go into the business world, it is your capital.

***

As I said, it wasn't long before I was back in the suit and tie.

One day, I was having a chat in a swanky New York City restaurant with one of the most renowned corporate lawyers of his era, a man named Marty.

"A lot of us lawyers wish we could be Harvard professors. You have a great role," Marty said. "Why would you leave now?"

I had just begun to outline privately to him my plans to leave Harvard—my two Dana-Farber labs, my teaching positions at Harvard Medical School and Harvard School of Public Health. Why? To accept a fulltime position as chairman and chief executive of another biotech startup.

As a professor of science you have all the skills you need to be a successful entrepreneur.

In many ways, I had to acknowledge, Marty was right. Why leave now? Funding was flooding into my HIV/AIDS lab. We were a world leader, unraveling more about the virus in the early '90s and identifying targets for drugs to contain it. Outstanding graduate students and visiting professors knocked on our doors. Invitations for keynote lectures arrived from around the world, far more than I could accept. I was juggling time with several companies, receiving supplemental income as leader of their scientific advisory boards.

"But," I explained to Marty, "I think I can change the future of medicine. I have been asked to take what we've learned about **genomics** in HIV research, apply advances in computing and robotics, and establish a business to sequence genomes for *every possible disease*. But I cannot do it within the university. This is going to take all of my time and energy. It's an opportunity of a lifetime, just too big to pass up."

But let's rewind a bit, to see how and why I got here. A fascinating man named Wallace Steinberg had been Johnson & Johnson's director of research, but left in frustration after many of his proposals to push the pharmaceutical giant faster into biotechnology were rejected. His belief in the future of biotechnology took him to Wall Street and the investment firm he organized in the 1980s called HealthCare Ventures. Wallace and I had worked extremely well together, respecting and trusting each other's expertise. Wally understood the pharmaceutical business and **venture capital**; I understood the science of biotechnology.

"Bill, I have an idea that will get you out of Harvard," he said one day.

"Wally, you're nuts. Why should I leave?" I said, a bit astonished at his suggestion. "I have a lifetime position at one of the greatest universities in the world. My work is going well. I love what I am doing there and what we are doing together."

We were sitting at the back table of a stylish Italian restaurant on Manhattan's Upper East Side. Wally had an extra gleam in his eye.

"Just a minute," he continued. "I want you to go to the National Institutes of Health and meet Craig Venter. He wants to leave NIH but only to work within a nonprofit institute that will commercialize his research."

Wally explained that he and a colleague were creating the institute—soon named the Institute for Genomic Research—and planning a private company to develop and market Venter's technology.

"Why me?" I asked, after raising some other concerns and questions, too. When I asked *why me?*, I was not fishing for compliments. Wally knew me better than that. He had determined, he said, that across his extensive network of scientists, research directors and pharmaceutical executives, I was the best fit for this role. Credentials: elite research discoveries in DNA molecular biology and the biochemistry of drug development. Proven leadership in fundraising and building teams and organizations in science and business.

"I know you well enough to believe that you can take full advantage of this opportunity," he said. "You will jump at the chance when you see what is possible."

His pitch was tempting. I did like jumping at chances…and I was getting restless at Harvard. Two years earlier, in 1990, NIH funding for HIV/AIDS was nearing two billion dollars and rising (to two-and-a-half billion dollars today). Excellent scientists from all over the world were fully engaged in AIDS research. I had trained many. Moreover, pharmaceutical and biotechnology companies were introducing new drugs almost monthly and my lab was filled with bright young scientists exploring many aspects of the virus and AIDS. I realized the pioneering phase of HIV/AIDS research was over, with one exception. The path ahead for HIV treatment was clear: continually developing drugs to keep pace with the virus mutations and combining them. Many able hands were at work. The one exception was the search for a vaccine to prevent HIV infection. At best, I reasoned then, that discovery would take another ten or twenty years. (And as we know, alas, there still is no HIV/AIDS vaccine.)

I thought: here is an opportunity to open a new frontier, why not take it?

"Wally may be right," I thought as the days passed. "If there really is a way to isolate human genes quickly, I can certainly figure out how to turn some of them into drugs. For any disease…"

I took Wally's advice and booked a trip to Washington D.C. where I'd meet with this Craig fellow at the NIH. Craig and I met over a brown bag lunch on an outdoor terrace in Bethesda, Maryland, not far from the sprawling campus of the National Institutes of Health, a half hour's drive north from Capitol Hill.

When he showed me computer printouts summarizing some of the first results of his rapid gene identification technique, I was stunned. There before me were descriptions of dozens of human genes. Some were similar to genes with well-known functions. Others were entirely new, unlike any seen before.

I thought: here is an opportunity to open a new frontier, why not take it?

In that instant, an epiphany swooped down before me, strong and almost glistening. I envisioned a sort of genie in a top hat. Top Hat Epiphany Genie was floating there an inch or two above the ground, fanning out three giant playing cards, each a displaying a consequence that would revolutionize medicine and medical science:

- Genomics would usher in a new era, opening new ways in medical science to find cures for most—if not all—disease.

- I would build a pharmaceutical company applying genomics to bring new drugs to market, demonstrating the potential of gene sequencing to identify molecular targets of vulnerability.

- Our success would inspire others to emulate our process, creating a strong infrastructure in genomics to fight disease and improve human health.

My vision of a genomics field within the rapidly expanding repertoire of biotechnology from nearly thirty years ago does not seem revolutionary today. But it was at that time in 1992. So, yes, it was a risk, but an appealing risk, the kind of risk that had the potential to save lives. A risk to feed my purpose, to improve human health. I immediately started brainstorming business strategies, for how to accomplish the above. I called Wally moments after that fateful brown bag lunch with Craig. I told him I would request a leave from Harvard to serve as chief executive for this new endeavor. The goal of the company would be to discover, develop and market new drugs. Licensing our technology to other companies would be a financing strategy. Wally and I discussed all the nuts and bolts, all my hesitations, and my conditions to remove them. I needed to know what he would commit to, and any issues that might give him pause. Once our positions were clear, and we had agreed, there was just one more question to settle.

"What name should we give the company?" he asked.

"I like Human Genome Sciences," I replied. "The name signals what we do, and why we are different."

"I like it, too," he said.

And so began Human Genome Sciences, where I served as the founding chairman and CEO for the next twelve years. Today, almost all drugs in the development pipelines of major pharmaceutical and biotechnology firms have their origin in the kind of genomics we practiced. Most cancer molecules are found this way, the targets for activating and directing the immune system to defeat specific cancer cells. Molecular biologists examine genes of immune cells that fight these cancers. If successful, the scientists determine the role of each cancer fighting antibody, manufacture them in high quantity and inject them in patients to attack cancer cells.

This is the essence of genomics and now the foundation of precision medicine: the use of chemical sequences in our genes to prevent disease and provide the most efficient and enduring therapies. Science as a superpower? You don't have to look any further for proof than what we accomplished for humanity and human health at Human Genome Sciences!

***

It is tempting for young scientists to think business is easier than science. It is not. Business is more challenging in many ways. You are not going to be prepared for business as a scientist until you understand human motivation. As an academic scientist you are in a particular bubble, relatively isolated or protected. Human society is infinitely complex. It has many varied pieces. You need to develop your understanding of different kinds of institutions and people.

There is no barrier in business for an expert to appear who is better than you. Often there will be. In business, there are geniuses who think exclusively about making money. The purpose of capital is to make more capital. These geniuses are dedicated to making more capital.

One day when you are in business, inevitably, you will find yourself across the table from one of these geniuses, maybe two or three, and you will be outshined. If you are a scientist you have a calling to do something different, some purpose that is not necessarily determined by money.

I believe young scientists should stay in their academic positions until they are well established, an expert in their field. Your knowledge and reputation take years to build as an academic scientist. Once your knowledge and reputation are established, they are unassailable.

If you believe a really big idea has come out of your research, ask yourself: What is the best tool to implement this idea? A university? A government lab? A startup company? A small company already established in the same field? A big company with massive research budgets conducting studies in the same field?

These are all wonderful tools. Analyze them for the best fit regarding your goal, your technology and which institutions would best enable your ideas to have the greatest impact in society.

And while we're back in advice mode, here's one grain of guidance I gave my Harvard students and colleagues— undergraduates, graduate students and postdocs alike: Treat everyone in your classes as if you are on a lifelong journey together because… you are. Make maximum efforts to stay on good terms with everyone you come across when you are young, because they are going to be with you when you are old.

It is not enough to focus only on what you do and what you do well. Help everybody around you to do as best as they can. People have broad networks and over time, people in those networks will ask about you.

Treat everyone in your classes as if you are on a lifelong journey together because… you are.

***

During the 1970s, I met a British virologist named George Poste whose cancer research at the University of Buffalo also examined DNA damage and repair. A Formula 5000 race driver in his young twenties, George was intense, brilliant and, literally and figuratively, hard-driving and highly caffeinated (consuming thirty cups of coffee daily!).

By the late '80s, now heading all research of newly merged pharmaceutical company SmithKline Beecham, he was keenly interested in our lab studies on potential HIV drug targets. I considered him a promising prospect for licensing access to our Human Genome Sciences genome data library. When I contacted George, he immediately agreed to meet with me.

Walking toward me under the vaulted marble arches in Union Station in Washington, George extended his hand vigorously and, before I said anything, exclaimed, "Hi, Bill! Let's make a deal!"

Well, that was easy…

Within two months of that handshake, we signed the largest single transaction of biotech's first two decades: one hundred twenty-five million dollars (!!) from SmithKline Beecham for exclusive rights to data we were rapidly assembling on human genes for drug development plus a seven percent stake in Human Genome Sciences **equity**.

Human Genome Sciences retained rights to use our data for our own drug discovery programs, but gave SmithKline the option to *develop* a drug first, if they wished to, from a specific gene. If they did not exercise that right within sixty days, we were free to go ahead. Business was shaping up to be pretty exciting.

George knew what he wanted before I said a word; I speculated he had at least two motivations. First, I knew from past dealings that George as a scientist had bold vision and favored big ideas; our idea was about as big as they come. He also was new in his job and wanted to make a strong impression; this deal checked that box as well.

I believe you can never convince anyone to do a deal. They must convince *themselves*. All you can do is offer an opportunity for them to have what they already know they want. You cannot change someone's perception of the world, their perception of you, or their will to do something. You cannot sell something to someone unless they believe they need it. George Poste understood what genomics would mean for drug development well before our stroll through Union Station. He had belief and will.

He wanted access to our data library for diagnostics and chemical discovery.

Either people are ready for a relationship with you or they are not. I believe that goes for every aspect of life.

***

With all this talk of deal-making and handshaking, we should probably pause for a very brief 101 on stocks and investments, both of which are key players in the game of business. As I mentioned, I didn't start out knowing much about finances. But it was important to acquire some know-how if I wanted to excel at business—which, given its new and integral connection to my purpose—I did.

Here's the basic(ish) scoop: the stock market is a place for investors (individuals, businesses, etc.) to buy and sell shares (in other words, little bits of ownership) in companies. It is a way for people to contribute to, and profit from, said companies. When you buy stock in a company, you are buying a share or shares. But unlike going to Target or the local chocolate shop, where everything has a fixed price, the price of stocks *changes* according to how high or low the demand for whatever it is that company is selling/doing. So, in the context of Human Genome Sciences, market conditions in the early 1990s were considered favorable because investors were eager to invest in biotech companies; the demand for our goods (data and technology) was high.

Another important piece of the financial puzzle is the idea of venture capital: the funding from outside investors in the early stages of a company's development, when it's all new and young and glittery, and promising return. Venture capital investments tend to be high risk (in other words: they put a lot of faith into the pot with their dough!), as they expect to see the business thrive. Venture capitalists, however, tend to be an impatient bunch, eager to see those chunky returns on their investment to compensate for putting their money in at the outset of the given company. One good way to return capital to these first investors who took the big risks of losing their money if the young company failed is to take a private company "public"; once a company's shares are publicly traded on a stock market, those shares can be cashed in.

Our financial progress at HGS was so rapid, and publicity around our unprecedented research concepts so intense, that pressure for a public offering began to mount as soon as the ink on our contract with SmithKline dried. Now was a good time. The market was up!

I pitched the idea to the board and they agreed, setting in motion plans for Human Genome Sciences to become a publicly traded company in less than four months, raising one hundred eighty million dollars on the final day of 1993, equal roughly to three hundred twenty million dollars today. For lack of a better word/sound-effect: *cha-ching*.

Over the next year, we expanded our licensing structure more broadly to other pharmaceutical companies, ultimately offering more opportunities for drug development worldwide and revenue from products that companies could develop and market from our data. Remember, we were in uncharted waters with our strategy at Human Genome Sciences, inventing a new way to discover drugs and then proposing to use our discoveries to bring new drugs to market.

There was strong interest in what knowledge of the genome might bring. Human Genome Sciences was featured in dozens of articles in business magazines and newspapers as well as the mainstream press, including cover stories in *Business Week* and *Forbes* as well as *Fortune*. I thought back to my first publication in *Science*. Of course this was a very different sort of coverage— from an academic paper to a media-business blitz—but I felt lucky and confident to have dipped my toe in both. The intersecting pathways between science and business were continuing to realize before my eyes.

The following years brought upon a roller-coaster of ups and downs (stock prices rising and falling, the **dot-com bubble**, a rocky presidential election) but our company's finances remained good and healthy. We proved in Human Genome Sciences that our brand of genomics could dramatically accelerate the search for genes and proteins as targets for new drugs to fight disease. When I began, I could identify no more than two hundred valid target genes and proteins in all of medicine. Two years later, that number had soared to several thousand.

In 2011, after sixteen years(!) of trials and development, Human Genome Sciences finally began to market the drug, Benlysta—the first new lupus treatment in over fifty years. Using genome data we identified, we created the design for this drug in the lab way back in the mid-'90s. Trials began in 2001 but it was long before the FDA could begin its review process and, eventually, approve Benlysta. News of the FDA approval sent Human Genome Sciences shares climbing in value, almost a hundred fold overnight. Isolating the chemistry for this drug was an important discovery, extremely important for lupus patients.

At HGS, we could identify new targets. What we could not do is accelerate *the process* of drug discovery. Companies still must identify new compounds, then conduct human trials to ensure their safety. That process remains long, costly, and extremely complex.

***

Human biology, the biology of any animal, is also extremely complex—the outcome of millions of years of evolution. Even today, we know just a teeny-tiny fraction of how the body actually works. My analogy for medical scientists is this: we are trying to throw a monkey wrench into a very complicated engine, closing one eye, hopping on one foot, and hoping it will work better.

When we were doing AIDS virus research, I described the challenge as the equivalent of asking a scientist or engineer around the year 1800 to figure out how a basic twentieth century television set worked. That scientist or engineer would take out one piece at a time and put it back, trying to figure out what went wrong when that single piece was removed. That is what we were doing with the AIDS virus. We broke one genetic piece at a time to see what happened.

We are trying to throw a monkey wrench into a very complicated engine, closing one eye, hopping on one foot, and hoping it will work better.

I often used these analogies in social settings, responding to people who asked why drug development took so long. "Where are all the drugs? Genomics looks like a failure." This happened often by the late '90s, a period when Human Genome Sciences had six drugs in development and our licensing partners had many of their own.

"What are you talking about?" I would respond. "Genomics is a huge success. It was not meant to solve the problem of getting new drugs quickly. It was meant to solve this problem: *how you start* to find drugs. That is what we did."

I predicted that the majority of new drugs within twenty to twenty five years would be based on the kind of genomics we did—into anatomy, cell physiology and pathology *to improve human health.* Mission accomplished…until of course, I set off on a new one.

***

Okay, I correct myself, the mission was not exactly *new*, the mission always remained—to improve human health. But! As you know by now: one *broad* mission can lead to many, many more exciting ones.

In 1999, I attended a conference in Italy where I was asked to speak (with just a few hours to prepare) about the future of medicine. Naturally, I wanted to address my go-to topics, biotechnology and genomics, but I also wanted to cover some newer — and potentially polarizing — topics of **stem cell research, tissue engineering and mind-machine interface**.

I paced around the hotel gardens, distracted by the lush green hills darkening now beyond the lake. Further away, I could see the fading rays of sun illuminating mountain peaks. "Soon, the leaves will drop," I thought, a bit wistfully. "This green will give way to the hard rock of winter. How fragile is life, how durable the stone."

Yet, in that instant, I was jolted by a concept so contradictory it registered almost like a physical blow.

"Wait! You have it backwards, Bill! It is *life* that endures and mountains that perish," I told myself. "A million years ago, an ocean where I stand was teeming with life. These majestic mountains will wear away and rise, once again to be covered by a soft living blanket. How many times in the last three-and-a-half billion years has this cycle repeated?" I asked myself. Then, more profoundly, "How can life endure as mountains perish?"

I felt a tingle from all this. Maybe it was the chilly Italian air and the faint smell of fresh bread but…I felt I was onto something. I continued to ponder.

"DNA, the immortal molecule," I thought. "All life is united by a single molecule, DNA, that has existed for billions of years, and may endure yet for billions of years to come. Yes, it takes different forms but all are variants of the original. One parent molecule divides and gives rise to two almost identical daughters. Both are originals. The immortal molecule continues its journey from the unimaginably distant past. We—all forms of life—are but its carriers, pausing briefly along the way."

"If the essence of life is immortality, why then do we as individuals perish? Might there be a way to link our individual existence to the fundamental immortality of life, the immortal DNA?

"Ah ha! I have my unifying concept," I realized. "Modern medicine seeks to restore our bodies to *normal*, whether injured by trauma, damaged by disease or worn by time. Isn't that what we really ask of medicine? To restore us to normal health, to be able to live and love in a healthy body and mind? Might the new medicine restore our mind and body and join our transient existence to our own unique immortal molecule?"

I decided to give this broad idea a name: *Regenerative Medicine*. To my mind, Regenerative Medicine captured the goal, not the means, and the goal is what is important. Confident and enthused and a touch tingly still, I began to plan my speech; I planned to explain all the different tools we use to achieve these goals of medicine's role in restoring human function. I also planned to explore the major frontiers of this new view of medicine:

- **Mechanical assists** such as steel rods for a damaged bone, metal plates to reinforce a spine, or acrylic glass lenses to restore vision;

- **Xeno-transplantation** such as organ transplants, stem cell technology, and tissue engineering;

- **Genomics**, with which you're now familiar—the study of a complete set of an organism's genes, in order to decipher the ways in which human cells themselves can lead to treatment;

- And last but certainly not least, and certainly the coolest, **the mind-machine interface**; the science-fiction-esque ability to connect signals directly from the brain via micro-chips to artificial limbs, in the case of accidents or injuries that result in unmoving muscles or amputations.

The talk that night after dinner was a success, and it roused some animated discussion about how/if to extend the human life span and the potentials of electronic thought transmission (in other words, mind-reading!). How fun and strange and wonderful it was, that a discussion of something like mind-reading could be grounded in practical science. And lest you forget about the ways in which science can be a superpower…well, here we have it.

Might the new medicine restore our mind and body and join our transient existence to our own unique immortal molecule?"

Regarding the extension of human life: I stated my belief that someday it will be possible to renew and repair most of our body… indefinitely. How far into the future will that be? I could not and still cannot say. I also am far less certain about our ability to renew and repair the brain. If we are able regrow parts of the aged or damaged brain, will the new functioning parts know what the old brain knew? All memory is encoded in an array of literally countless neuron connections. Will the new tissue reconnect with that network? (Twenty years later, we still are not able to answer that question.)

What about the ethics of achieving much longer lived, if not immortal, generations? We do not question the set of technologies that allowed the average lifespan around the world to double in the past century. I doubt that we will question the ethics of technologies that allow us to double lifespan yet again in the century to come. (Currently, a natural healthy lifespan is estimated to be … are you ready for this?… one hundred twenty-five years!) Extended lifespans will arise slowly across the centuries, one millennium at a time. I cannot speak for what future generations will judge to be ethical. For myself, I believe it ethical to extend healthy aging as long as possible. If nothing else, for all the movies I still want to see, and books I still want to read!

And regarding the reading of thoughts and interpreting electrical brain signals, I told my listeners: If we can figure out intention and action, which we can, then I do believe it is feasible to decode our thoughts, spoken or unspoken. It may even be possible without penetrating the skull.

The exciting and stirring reactions to my presentation were gratifying. Several participants asked what they could do to help; others, how I intended to develop this new field. Once I returned to the States I quickly recruited an American bioengineer who was also a urologist and pediatric surgeon to organize the first Society for Regenerative Medicine and join me in editing a new online journal for the field, *e-Biomed: The Journal of Regenerative Medicine*. That bioengineer, Dr. Anthony Atala, and I co-chaired several annual conferences for scientists, physicians, journalists and bioethicists. Today, arrays of societies advance new knowledge through conferences and journals for various branches of the field. Many if not most medical schools, institutes and universities around the world now include departments of regenerative medicine. Mission accomplished, continued, and expanded.

I thought: Fantastic, but…what now?

(But hmm, maybe you were reading my mind, and already knew what I was thinking.)

CHAPTER 9

Health for All, Far and Near

In 2004, I turned 60. I received some really nice presents to mark the occasion, but more memorable than gifts was my leap into the world of global health philanthropy. That year, I stepped down as Human Genome Science's chairman and chief executive and decided to feed my ever-hungry travel bug. This time, though, my travels were not driven by wanderlust or scientific research; rather, I traveled with the goal of visiting the best healthcare systems in the world and the outstanding medical centers within those systems. I was searching for ideas on how to deliver high quality care at a low cost that I could bring back to the United States. How's that for a souvenir?

During a trip to India I found something that amazed me: a hospital conducting hundreds of thousands of cataract (a condition in which the eye lens loses vision due to progressive opacity) operations annually with outstanding results, the vast majority *for free*. Actual cost per operation, including materials, supplies, physician time and overhead? About thirty U.S. dollars. How could that be? In the United States, we were charging patients thousands for the same surgery!

After touring the hospital and talking to the doctors doing the surgeries, I realized how they had managed to do it: a relentless focus on efficiency and cost control, that's how. For example, operating rooms had two tables, not one. As a physician operates on a patient at one table, the next patient is prepped on the other. When the first operation is finished, the physician turns around to begin the next one. One physician might perform as many as fifty cataract operations each day!

At the time, Aravind Eye Hospital's small network of hospitals had nearly fifteen hundred beds. Twelve hundred were provided at *zero cost* for people with no means to pay, and another three hundred for patients who could afford rates that matched other nearby hospitals. One of the surgeons, Aravind Srinivasan, suggested I visit a few of India's leading hospitals for cardiac surgery. There, he said, I would discover surgeons typically perform more than *a thousand* surgeries a year, averaging a few thousand dollars each. In the United States, surgeons might do *one hundred* open heart procedures a year, each costing many tens of thousands of dollars. *What gives?!*, I thought.

I knew India was advancing rapidly, lifting three hundred million from poverty into the economic middle class over the previous three decades. Their remarkable medical facilities and procedures inspired me. I now could visualize how my global health ambitions might take shape: I must learn about the most cost efficient medical practices in India, and bring them back to the U.S. Surely, I thought, that will be a way to lower costs and improve access and affordability in the U.S. healthcare system.

As you likely know, our healthcare system here in the U.S. has been—and still is— flawed in many ways; many Americans are without healthcare, and the disparities between different populations are extreme. We've seen this with COVID-19—some groups have had a much harder time accessing tests, treatment and care than others. Even though we have some of the best medical centers in the *world*, not everyone in the U.S. can access the high quality care being offered.

This inequality is a grave injustice and for the past fifteen years, I've worked to close that gap here in the U.S. and around the world. Disease is more prevalent in a society that goes to the doctor less. Spending *should* focus on medical research and preventative medicine so that disease is less severe, prevalent, and costly in the future.

In inefficient health care systems, ultimately, it does not matter what treatments you have. Most people do not have access to them. So, what good is biotechnological advancement if the breakthrough is unable to help those that need it? In countries like the U.S., we spend way too much money at the end of the process—health care services—and starve the beginning of the process: basic research and disease prevention.

In inefficient health care systems, ultimately, it does not matter what treatments you have. Most people do not have access to them.

After an academic career devoted to discovery research and a second career as a biopharmaceutical executive, I realized that year, back in 2004, that the sharply rising cost of healthcare was a threat to both of those endeavors: scientific discovery and biomedical innovation. Moreover, it was clear that the discoveries and products of biomedical science were not benefiting most people.

I was finally able to act on this insight when I created ACCESS Health International, a not-for-profit operating foundation designed to speed the day when everyone, no matter where they live, no matter their age, has access to high-quality, affordable healthcare.

***

Why is she suffering and how can I help? Is there anything I can *actually* do?

You recall how those thoughts shook me deeply, when I stood beside my mother's bed at not quite four years old. I never forgot. So too in Calcutta, when I picked my way through crowds of the sick and the suffering. You remember as well how I vowed then to do whatever I could to heal the sick of the world. I never forgot.

Now was the time for me to focus directly on global health. I had been invited before leaving Human Genome Sciences to consider roles as a university president, a medical sciences professor and a consultant a at a biotech venture fund. But these were too far afield for what I knew I wanted: bringing high quality, affordable care to as many people as possible.

Instead, I teamed with a seasoned business adviser based in India, John Michael Lind, and we established ACCESS Health International. Our mission was to become a think tank, studying best practices in healthcare services, and an advisory service for people in government or the private sector who shared our objective.

We set up headquarters in Hyderabad—the "City of Pearls" it's called— situated along the banks of Musi River in southern India. To lead that office, we brought on a recent graduate of Sweden's Stockholm School of

Economics. Sofi Bergkvist had worked on health issues in India and Malawi, and at the United Nations in New York. She was eager and committed, willing to move to Hyderabad and organize the office. For ten years, as an ACCESS Health executive director, Sofi helped us build offices in India and Singapore and conducted studies in Bangladesh, Brazil, Sweden and eventually China and the Philippines.

Our approach had two parts. The first part was to find the best examples of healthcare service in the world, try to understand them deeply, rigorously, then describe them in reports that could become an effective tool to help people around the world interested in replicating these models. We worked hard to capture knowledge. The second part was to identify government officials who genuinely wanted to improve healthcare delivery and encourage them to adopt these proven models.

Why focus on governments? It has to do, yet again, with money. Policy precedes money. Consider: the U.S. government spends more than three trillion dollars annually on healthcare; the pharmaceutical industry budgets roughly ninety billion dollars annually for research; and the largest foundation dedicated to global health, the Bill & Melinda Gates Foundation, commits roughly five billion dollars a year. We focus on government because that's where the biggest money is.

We believe that government is the strongest tool available for improving global health. If we can influence government policy to do various things—to spend money a little bit better—we have done something. A little bit of science can solve a problem for hundreds of millions of people. You can do the same thing, improve the lives of hundreds of millions of people, if you hit the policy right. This is harder than science; you need both patience and resources to work with so many people with varying opinions and influence. But if I had to guess, I'd say: you've got this.

> *We believe that government is the strongest tool available for improving global health.*

ACCESS Health began as an experiment, an initial investment with the idea that if early projects worked, they would become self-sustaining and continue. We viewed each project internally as an experiment with many uncertainties, and looked for talented people willing to take a chance. As we explored a bit in the previous chapter, this is the venture capitalist's approach. Each project depends upon circumstance and funding, but the main task is finding talented young people and giving them freedom to pursue their dreams.

It was like leading a university research department. You hire talented scientists. They support themselves with government or private funding. You judge people by performance. Not everything will work out as planned. When it does not, just as with a laboratory research hypothesis or a startup company's initial product strategy, you adapt. And adapt I did. I had to.

Alas (and I'll say it— annoyed!), I found little interest at all in the United States or Europe in learning from India's health systems innovations. A typical reaction: "That is an impressive story but will never work here. Everything they do, we know how to do." After some probing, I concluded that this was a coded message, another indictment in my view against the U.S. health system: "We have no need to be more efficient. We are making plenty of money doing what we do. Why should we change?" Sigh.

For the first five years, I spent half of my time in different countries, absorbing their cultures, their healthcare issues and working with *people*. We always looked for people in government, nonprofits or the private sector who were eager to make positive changes. I realized years before that it was a waste of time attempting to persuade people who were skeptics or otherwise passive about my ideas. You can never implant motive in another human being.

***

A few months after we opened in Hyderabad, waiting rooms in nearby hospitals were suddenly overflowing. The chief minister of the state, Andhra Pradesh, had declared that everyone below the poverty line was entitled to free hospital medical care. Eighty percent of the state's eighty million people qualified... *sixty-four million people.*

Here was a golden opportunity, right outside our doors, to study a health system transitioning as fast as humanly possible to serve the poor. Most of these patients had never before been evaluated by a nurse or physician. Patients needed only to present identification papers to be admitted.

The program—called Aarogyasri—covered nearly a thousand medical and surgical procedures for ailments affecting the heart, liver, kidney, lung and pancreas as well as burns or birth defects. The state would pay full costs, generating revenues to cover the costs from an increase in liquor sales taxes. Smart! All public and private hospitals were enrolled as care providers if they met minimum requirements of quality. These public and private care providers were reimbursed at the same rates. The funds flowed back from the government typically within weeks of filings, in contrast to what often had taken a year or more before the policy change.

In English, Aarogyasri translates as "health for all," an uncanny expression of my purpose to improve human health and our belief at ACCESS Health that *all* individuals have a right to affordable high quality healthcare and to lead healthy and productive lives.

Foundations in the United Kingdom, Germany, Canada and Sweden wanted to know how Aarogyasri worked. So did the Gates and Rockefeller Foundations in the United States and the World Bank. Each provided funding for reports we developed. We were in the right place at the right time, which shows you again that taking initiative to achieve your vision creates unforeseen opportunity. Many neighboring states in India were interested as well. We soon figured out how we could share what we were learning in Andhra Pradesh to others in central and southern India. We gained experience and expertise to advise in healthcare finance, governance, quality assurance, supply chain management, medical audit and management. Meanwhile, other programs were underway for improving the efficiency and affordability of swift and reliable ambulance services (which had been tragically absent in earlier years when, if you had a serious accent, it'd take you several hours and several modes of bumpy transportation before arriving at a hospital.)

We were in the right place at the right time, which shows you again that taking initiative to achieve your vision creates unforeseen opportunity.

To this day, I still love traveling all over India. This is the most diverse country in the world. Imagine: there are twenty-two official languages! Currency is printed in eleven different languages! Yet there is a unity of common beliefs. It would be fabulous if our entire world could achieve this same unity. Moreover, India has a huge land mass....equal to all of Europe, which spans from northern Africa northward to the Arctic Ocean and eastward from the Atlantic Ocean to the Ural Mountains of Russia.

As we were getting started in India, I came across more opportunities in Singapore about two thousand miles away at the southern tip of Malaysia and beside the South China Sea. Singapore's economy had been solidly established among the world's strongest, and rising, leaders of this nation of six million people were looking to biotechnology as a launch pad for more economic growth. Their government was about to open an expansive research center futuristically named Biopolis, and it had lured many outstanding scientists to head laboratories there and was planning more investments. I spent a week touring Biopolis and several corporate laboratories, and that trip gave me a clearer understanding of Singapore's commitments. The facilities were world class. Highly accomplished scientists tackling major problems. I was impressed, and while many ACCESS Health projects were flourishing in India, I increasingly kept my eye on Singapore.

Wouldn't that be a good hub for us to expand, not only in Singapore but also more widely in the region of southeast Asia? To Thailand, Cambodia, Myanmar, Laos and Vietnam?

So you could imagine my delight when an invitation came in 2010 to attend a kickoff meeting for what Singapore's government framed as its Initiative to Improve Health in Asia. That theme sounded ambitious for such a small nation, but not after I heard the longtime health minister, Khaw Boon Wan, describe spectacular results of Singapore's own health system.

Singaporeans enjoyed such high levels of quality health that the nation ranked among the world's ten best by any major measure, achieved with total spending by government and the private sector on health slightly above four percent. I could hardly believe what I heard. At the time, the U.S. was spending seventeen percent of

GDP on health (soon to rise to where it has remained for the past few years, at eighteen percent) with Americans receiving significantly lower overall quality of health, ranking far below all other industrialized nations.

"What a great example... proof of principle that high quality affordable healthcare is achievable," I thought, listening with amazement, my ears almost hot with excitement. "I should study this in detail. What I learn may be valuable to others, especially back home."

***

After studying Singapore's system—its high functionality as well as its eventual issues with financial sustainability and maintaining good care for the elderly—my thoughts turned to Sweden. To my surprise, Sweden was bedeviled by failures in caring for its elderly population. Unsafe conditions in eldercare homes had contributed to a political party's defeat and fall from power years earlier. "The world looks to Sweden as a leader in healthcare best practices," I noted. "If they are having problems it is a warning for others. Let's write a book to help people avoid the most obvious problems."

Our interviews with pioneers in Sweden's eldercare professions quickly surfaced major problems: lack of coordination between social and healthcare workers; unmet hopes of aging people to live longer in their homes, supported by home care; unsolved challenges of caring for elderly with Alzheimer's disease, dementia and related cognitive declines. We soon broadened the study to examine best practices for eldercare and dementia care in the United States and elsewhere in Europe: Germany, the Netherlands, Norway and Finland. Our major findings on eldercare and dementia? Provide care wherever and whenever a person needs assistance; integrate care in all aspects of a person's life; and create purpose by encouraging community engagement and lifelong learning for older persons. Structure environments to encourage autonomy; make use of new technologies, including robot companions, to improve quality of life.

With the enormous help and insight from ACCESS Health colleagues Sofia Widen, Jean Galiana and Anna Dirksen, we wrote and published two books on the ways in which healthcare programs and technology can—and must!—help humans age with dignity. How can we live until age one hundred twenty-five, watching all those movies and reading all those books, if we're not well taken care of?

The healthcare responses we chronicled, though, are only first steps. Can the **private sector** play a role in solving these issues? Absolutely. In Sweden, we conceived of a business incubator for startups addressing problems of the elderly, especially people with declining cognitive ability. "There is even a Swedish fund, the Post Code Lottery, that will support us," said our ACCESS Health leader in Stockholm, Stephanie Treschow. "Great idea, Stephanie!" I said as she outlined the plan. "Go for it!" This thrill I felt was akin to my early days working in labs—here were intelligent, driven individuals fighting not only to fulfill their own purpose, but also the purpose of the group, the company, the country, the world!

Our Modern Aging program, which Stephanie conceived and proposed, quickly took wing in Singapore as well, and then Beijing and Shanghai. Funds from the Singapore government and ACCESS Health provided seed capital for more than twenty companies. These startups developed new technologies for care of the elderly and mentally ill. As the program wound down in 2019, our new leader in Singapore, Sejal Mistry, breathed new life into our initial strategy: to advise and strengthen health systems across southeast Asia. Further east, we maintain an office in the Philippines, conducting research and advising the Health Ministry and local governments and private enterprises.

Our signature effort across southeast Asia in those years, Modern Aging, also set the tone for our programs in

China. We described it as an ecosystem of innovation to address the needs of the elderly. We have offices now in Beijing, Shanghai and Hong Kong, working often with a community of entrepreneurs and business leaders, supporting them with deep knowledge about best practices in eldercare. Our focus is on innovation, technologies and new models for delivering and paying for health services.

***

ACCESS Health is continuously evolving. At the beginning of 2020, right before COVID-19 swept across the world, I took a trip to Rwanda with our India country director, Dr. Krishna Reddy. Krishna and I have known each other a long time. He's a cardiologist with a long and distinguished career, marked by his leadership of the CARE Hospital Group which he helped create. The hospital group is perhaps the most advanced, complete cardiac care center in the country. The hospitals have become models for patient satisfaction and innovation.

Krishna and I were traveling to Rwanda to meet up with an American named Paul Farmer. Paul had grown up all over the United States, spending a few years here and there in places like Birmingham, Alabama and Brooksville, Florida. For a while he lived on a houseboat in the Gulf of Mexico and in an old school bus his father converted into a mobile home. No matter where he was living, he always excelled in school. He was elected president of his senior class in high school and won a full scholarship to Duke University in North Carolina. At Duke, he studied the sciences, eventually landing on a major in medical anthropology—a field where you look at the relationship between, health, disease and the culture and environment that people are living in. Eventually, Paul was hit by that travel bug too. After graduating from Duke and completing a short fellowship at the University of Pittsburgh, he decided he would spend a year working in a public health clinic in Haiti, the poorest country in the Western hemisphere.

He tended to the sickest of the sick and the poorest of the poor and, in doing so, he started to find his own calling: improving the health of the world's poorest and sickest communities. While he was in Haiti, Farmer found out he'd been accepted to Harvard Medical School—his dream!—but he couldn't imagine leaving the people and the work he had started. So he decided to do both. He would travel to Cambridge for exams and laboratory practices, and then pack up his books and travel back to Haiti where he would work in the clinic and finish off the rest of his studies on his own. During that time he was talking to anyone who would listen about the goal that had been forming in his mind: bringing the benefits of modern medical science to those most in need.

Eventually Farmer and four other friends decided to create their own organization, Partners In Health. The work that Farmer and his friends had done in Haiti, their grassroots gumption, combined with their commitment to health as a social good and human right landed Partners In Health opportunities everywhere from Malawi and Sierra Leone to Mexico and Peru.

In Rwanda, Partners In Health supported all avenues of health service delivery: community health workers, community health centers, district hospitals, and district leadership. They built a new hospital that offered specialized treatment centers and surgical programs, including a neonatal intensive care unit and a mental health specialty clinic run by government employed psychiatric nurses and a psychologist—one example of a nationwide effort, another partnership between Partners In Health and the Ministry of Health, to integrate mental health care into primary care. They had also created the Butaro Cancer Center of Excellence, Rwanda's first public cancer center.

Paul Farmer, Krishna Reddy and I, with doctors at the University of Global Health Equity in Rwanda

Perhaps the most impressive of all their endeavors though was their medical and public health school called the University of Global Health Equity. The University invites aspiring health professionals from across the country and around the world to learn about health systems from a wide array of overlapping perspectives: the medical, the social, the managerial. Students can combine this education with prior personal and professional experiences to cultivate a global perspective of their own—a vision, the seed of global health leadership. Krishna and I both understood immediately just how important this project would be. The entire university was an invitation to the next generation of thinkers to jump in and make a change.

***

What's *your* current goal? Can you play a role in solving big health issues? Let me answer this one for you...absolutely. Our purpose in life is what defines us, not the schools we go to or the degrees we earn. While academic achievement can get the ball rolling, the definition of one's self should not be so simple. Purpose should be a driving force behind self-fulfillment.

My time at Harvard, Berkeley, and elsewhere was formative, insightful, and educational. Those experiences unveiled the world of biophysics that I fell in love with and, more importantly, led me to understand my purpose: furthering advancements in biotechnology to improve health outcomes for the world and all its inhabitants. But you know what else was formative, insightful, and educational? All the books I read as a child, all the time I spent at museums with my kids, and all the places in the world where I've been lucky enough to travel—every experience is an opportunity to refine our purpose in life, a new opportunity to see the world from a different point of view.

In Rwanda, as important as the trip to the clinics and university was to my vision to improve human health, some of the biggest lessons were the ones I learned after I left Paul and Partners and Health. The university was not far from the Volcanoes National Park in Rwanda, which is home to the famous mountain gorillas—those gentle great apes who touched the hearts of people around the world thanks to the efforts of conservationist and primatologist Dian Fossey. My wife Maria Eugenia and I decided to plan a trip to see them. We climbed for hours through thickets of bamboo just for a glimpse of these shy animals. And when we arrived… well, there are no words really to describe looking into the eyes of another species and seeing our own selves reflected back.

Every experience is an opportunity to refine our purpose in life, a new opportunity to see the world from a different point of view.

When Fossey began her work with the gorillas back in 1966, they were a dying breed. Poaching, disease and the loss of their habitat eventually reduced their number to just 250. But thanks to Fossey's work—her *vision* to study and protect these great creatures—there are now nearly 1000 of these majestic animals living in the conservation area in the region. One person, with a singular purpose, who changed the world. Sound familiar?

It doesn't matter what you choose to do in life (though I *do* hope you at least consider the field of science) what matters most is finding your purpose. Once you set your goal, then everything else becomes an opportunity to help you achieve it— a chance meeting or a seemingly irrelevant piece of data becomes a missing piece in a puzzle that moves you ever closer to your dream.

Knowledge and achievement are like waves, pushing and pulling you. A wave is not the enemy of a ship; it pushes you forward as much as it may push you back. If you are good at recognizing these waves, you can time them just right, so you surf them, and they push you forward with enormous force.

Some may have the fortune of larger waves through privilege or hard work. Yet, the waves do not define you. The fulfilled life is one where you ride your waves as best you can. Try to live your life with a purpose in mind. Use the tools at your disposal to work towards that purpose. And we all must work together to give everyone their wave. If everyone worked with this mindset, who knows what we could achieve? Who knows the lasting impact a surfer waiting on their wave could make?

***

As you know, when I first organized ACCESS Health International, my hope was to help improve the quality, cost and efficiency of care in the United States by learning about the best healthcare examples in other countries. As pleasing as our success in India, China, Singapore and other countries became, I never gave up hope that we might someday include U.S. examples in our research, publishing and advisory work. Then that opportunity came, unexpectedly, right in my home city of New York.

New York University's health center had lagged badly in rankings for the quality of its patient care, medical school and medical research around 2000. Even worse, by 2007 the financial stability of NYU itself, one of America's finest academic institutions, was threatened by the medical center's mounting losses. Then: a new dean and CEO was hired. An unexpected and much-needed hero. He was an unusual choice, with none of the typical credentials for leading an academic medical center; he had no prior business experience and he'd never been trained or mentored as a manager. In fact, Dr. Robert Grossman had never managed anything larger than his NYU radiology department.

Grossman was in his sixth year at the medical center's helm in 2013 when he agreed to meet in his New York office and hear my Shanghai proposal. He listened, then said, "I have no interest in creating a new medical school and hospital in China. I am focused like a laser on building the best hospital and medical school in New York."

Laser focus was something I recognized and respected. Grossman demonstrated how one leader with a vision for excellence and accountability could transform the culture and elevate the performance of an institution. The scale and rate of improvement during his first ten years leading NYU Medical Center were remarkable. He catapulted a financially failing institution into one of the nation's best medical centers. Every decision must answer one question: Will this improve patient care? Nursing schedules. Executive and dean hirings and promotions. Emergency department staffing. Elevator maintenance. Ambulance routes. Lighting. Everything... *Will this improve patient care?* (If you've ever broken a bone or had a surgery, you know how important it is to feel comfortable and well-cared for at the hospital. Shockingly, many hospitals make patients feel *worse*, not better.)

Grossman, upbeat and unflappable, asserted that NYU Medical Center would become, "a world class, patient-centered, integrated academic medical center." It sure did. The center soon was renamed NYU Langone Health in the wake of a two hundred million dollar donation by Ken Langone (founder of the best place in which to kill a few hours—Home Depot!) and his wife Elaine.

I tell you all this not because I love NYC and Home Depot (which I do) but because it's another prime example of how immense change can emerge from the passion of a single individual. With that laser focus on accountability and transparency, Bob Grossman enabled NYU Langone to thrive in the way of leadership, quality, data, ambulatory care, and financial efficiency and clarity. I believe all leaders of healthcare systems should follow Grossman's example; further, I believe they should adapt and embrace his foremost principles for success: culture, vision, integrated care, real-time data, quality, safety, and self-reliance. Quite a list. Grossman prioritized them all and to see it all in action was a great gift of my career.

I am convinced that NYU Langone's proven approach, Bob Grossman's approach, can help communities anywhere in the country accomplish what we all want and urgently need: high quality healthcare at lower cost.

***

Archimedes said, "Give me a lever long enough and I can move the earth." We are not privileged in ACCESS Health to have such levers. But, like a diamond cutter, we can find a fault in the stone, make a tap and break apart the toughest diamond.

That is the way I think about what I am doing now: working to understand where to make those taps and achieve the biggest change... to apply my accumulated knowledge. Small leverage for big change.

CHAPTER 10

The Golden Key

Nature really came for us in 2020, didn't it? Sometimes, when nature comes for us, it means a big fun snowstorm (hopefully followed by a big fun snow day); sometimes it means an earthquake or an eruption or a beautiful meteor shower. In early 2020, however, nature came for us in the form of a virus, SARS-CoV-2, and the disease that it causes, COVID-19. When those early rumblings of a new pneumonia-like illness in Wuhan, China rumbled through, my sense of purpose flashed red. Just as in that summer of 1985. A continuous loop ran through my thoughts, "This is it!"... a second imperative to capture the world's attention, to be heard, to push our leaders to deliver the resources and respect for science required to control this pandemic.

Though few were aware of it at the time, the first rumblings actually began at the end of 2019 when ophthalmologist Li Wenliang alerted a group of fellow doctors about the possibility of an outbreak. He worked in Wuhan with patients and saw the devastation on the way; he urged his colleagues to take protective measures.

Days after sending his missive, he was accused by the Public Security Bureau in Wuhan for making false statements, disturbing order and creating panic. In a matter of just weeks, Wenliang contracted the virus and lost his life to it. He was only thirty-three years old. Shortly before he died, he lamented the lack of medical transparency worldwide. To me, this is a sorrowful example of how many lives are often lost when the world fails to pay attention to the people trying to make a difference. Dr. Li sounded an alarm, and his warnings went unheeded. I think about his heroism just about every day.

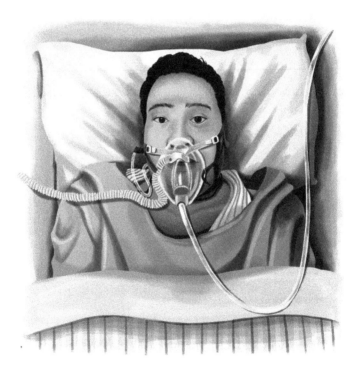

At the time of this writing, COVID-19 has gone on to infect more than one hundred million people worldwide and can be tied to more than two million deaths. The impact of the pandemic has been and will continue to be massive, and it will likely change our behaviors for generations to come. Is the handshake gone forever? Will masks be here to stay? The ball pit at indoor play centers? Hugs?? Thankfully, I think hugs will make a comeback.

My personal losses have been far fewer than what many have suffered. Yet COVID-19 has still completely upended my life. After a lifetime spent in science, medicine and pursuing better public health, I find myself once again logging eighteen hour days (I am a bit tired!) battling a new disease. I am working closely with three generations of students—my former students, their former students and those who studied under them—to understand the virus. Together, and along with many in the private sector I've worked with over the years, we are doing what we can to create new diagnostic tests, new drugs and new vaccines.

But equally important to the work I've been doing with scientists laboring away in their labs, is the work I've been doing with political leaders laboring away in government offices. Just like every Iron Man needs his Avengers, every scientist needs a team of superheroes who can help them get the job done. What good is a Covid-19 vaccine if no one has access to it? Or HIV treatments if no one can afford to take them? Perhaps the only superpower greater than science is the power of government to make sure everyone—no matter where they live or how much they earn—has access to all the benefits that science can offer.

I've been asked by governments worldwide—in Europe, Asia, the Middle East, Africa and here in the United States—for advice on the best policies and containment measures. This brings me no end of joy, as it's a recognition of how important science—and scientists— are to the greater good. When I was a little kid running around chasing snakes in the Mojave desert, scientists reigned supreme. Those were years right after World War II and right at the beginning of the Cold War between the United States and Russia (or the Soviet Union as it was known then). A leading edge in science was considered a matter of life or death. Science helped us create better weapons, faster missiles, and superior defenses—it also drove us to explore the outer reaches of space. There was even an official Science Advisor position in government, giving direct advice to the President on issues as wide ranging as the economy, national security, and the design of the US census.

But somewhere in the mid-1970s (think Nerf balls and video Pong), that started to change. We had won the war, proven ourselves to be leaders in science and technology, and held a strong belief that our scientific supremacy was enough to keep all threats — whether from man or nature — at bay. Over time, the role of science lost its standing and the Presidential Science Advisor position terminated in 1973. When it returned three years later, it had lost much of its influence.

Perhaps the only superpower greater than science is the power of government to make sure everyone—no matter where they live or how much they earn—has access to all the benefits that science can offer.

Guess what? COVID-19 changed all that. Once again, science is recognized as the superpower it is. In fact, for the first time in history, a scientist now sits on the Cabinet of the United States—that's a big promotion! Elevating the US Office of Science and Technology Policy to a Cabinet-level agency signals an important shift — science will once more play a prominent role within the highest circles of government.

COVID-19 didn't just change how policymakers viewed science, it also changed how scientists viewed their own work. When COVID-19 forced a near global lockdown and the world closed down, new relationships opened up. Science can be a competitive business. Remember those stories of my Harvard colleagues and I desperately hunting down funding for our work on HIV? Well, too many scientists competing for too few dollars tends to breed a sense of rivalry—you want credit for your work because that's what's going to help secure your next round of funding. It's true in business, as well. Pharmaceutical companies, for example, invest millions of dollars in new technologies that may—if the company is lucky—lead to lifesaving (and moneymaking) products and treatments. Most of the time, if you know you're close to a breakthrough or you make a discovery that can give you an important advantage, you keep those cards held tight to your chest.

But with COVID-19, the concern over what this new disease could do to all of us, to our entire species, was so great and so profound that all the walls that divided us came quickly tumbling down. Nobody cared about academic credit, nobody cared about making the first buck, everyone in the scientific community, everywhere in the world, just cared about saving lives. Within weeks of the illness being discovered, long before COVID-19 even had its name, scientists in China released an initial genome sequence of a new coronavirus they suspected of causing the disease. The data, which was decoded in China, gained global attention thanks to a virologist in

Sydney, Australia who knew of the Chinese scientists' work and tweeted a link to the sequence they'd published online.

That one tweet was like a Bat Signal over Gotham City— all the superheroes around the world suited up and jumped into action. An evolutionary biologist in Edinburgh, Scotland figured out that the virus was very similar to SARS. A researcher in New York published the new virus' phylogenetic tree. Another researcher in North Carolina started trying to reverse-engineer a live virus from the sequence so that other scientists could start to develop antibody tests. And that was just the first 24 hours. This unprecedented global scientific collaboration continues to this day. It is thanks to the scientists working together in labs all across the world that, just one year after the disease was discovered, vaccines that could protect us from illness were already developed and being rolled out. Sooner or later (thankfully, sooner in this case), science will always save us.

What we're doing to control the pandemic today is more important than just this one disease. It's about how we respond to any challenge that confronts us as a species. If we are to survive, and to *thrive,* we need to marshal all our resources and work together to overcome any challenge that comes our way. COVID-19 laid bare the true power of science. Science is a superpower, and COVID-19 was our latest supervillain. And what do superheroes do against supervillains? They win.

Sooner or later (thankfully, sooner in this case), science will always save us.

***

The opportunities and powers that scientists have are endless. When you're a scientist, people are interested in what you have to say. People want to learn from you. People want to be *saved* by you. Science is a big part of our world, and people who are interested in the world are interested in science. As a scientist, if you do it well, you have a golden key. You can use that key to open doors that will take you in whatever directions you choose.

If you want to change society as a scientist, you need to work through many powerful institutions—think tanks, major corporations, non-profits, government agencies, academia, the news media. You can build personal networks that over time become valuable for gaining influence and shaping policies. Many people who take on these roles overlap in many organizations, including the arts.

Once you have this role advising governments and other institutions, you begin to realize how tightly the world is linked! A few people with important knowledge have inordinate influence and impact—sometimes for better, sometimes for worse. In time, and to my surprise, leaders from a much wider range than I anticipated—of nations, industries, professions, humanitarian causes and more— sought my advice. I traveled at their invitations around the country and around the world.

When I leapt into the breakneck AIDS funding campaign in 1985, I already grasped many levers for influencing public policy. Marshaling key facts. Writing articles. Briefing journalists. Informing local communities. Communicating. Persuading. Convincing. All elements of the craft that I put into action during those antiwar protests and campaigns in the '60s and '70s. Alongside heroes, I played a big role in those early years helping to speed up the process. It is a wonderful, astonishing, and extremely validating feeling to know that I was able to do that.

High honors in science come about ten years after you have done the work. Many scientists—most scientists— will stick to one field, get recognized, and stay in their lane. As you've seen, mine has been a bit of a multi-lane highway, a zig zag. But zig zags garner many a reward, personal and professional. As you might recall from my introduction, *TIME Magazine* included me on its 2001 list of the "25 Most Influential Global Business Executives." In 2015, *Scientific American* named me one of the hundred most influential leaders in biotechnology. The Biotechnology Association, Ernst & Young (now known as EY) and other organizations honored me with their top awards. Invitations, inquiries and requests poured in as I became recognized for my hard work and dedication. Recognition is a tool that helps you get things done. And we can thank—I certainly do—curiosity, passion, and parallax vision for propelling it all forward.

***

One day years ago one of my former PhD students who was doing important research on viruses asked me to have lunch: "What did you do to get on all these boards and councils?" she asked. "How does all of this happen, Bill? What do you think I should be doing?"

"Well, you really cannot 'apply' for these opportunities, if that's what you mean," I said. "But as you get to be better known from your research, you will be invited to become part of many decision making bodies, and often advise on and recommend policy. When you work toward your purpose, you insert yourself into these streams and doing so will provide the people, the prospects, and all the tools you'll need to do *anything and everything* you set out to accomplish!"

Then I told her what I told you earlier about the golden key: as a scientist, the golden key is yours.

And too, the *powers*.

Glossary of Terms

Aldehydes: An organic compound which contains a formyl group (a part of a molecule which produces an odorous, colorless gas) formed by the oxidation of alcohols. It is made of a carbon double bonded to oxygen.

Amino Acids: Simple organic compounds which make up the building blocks of proteins.

Antiproton: A very small particle subatomic particle of the same mass as a proton, but with a negative electric charge.

Big Bang: The cosmological theory in which the rapid expansion of matter from a state of extremely high density and temperature formed the universe as we know it.

Calvin cycle: The series of chemical reactions that occur in chloroplasts (super tiny parts of plant cells) during photosynthesis (the process by which plants and microorganisms use heat/energy from sunlight to turn carbon dioxide into glucose and oxygen).

Cell differentiation: The process by which a cell changes from one cell type to another. Usually, the cell changes from less specialized to more specialized. Differentiation happens many times during the development of a multicellular organism (i.e. a human) as it evolves from a simple zygote to a complex system of tissues and cell types.

Centrifuge: A piece of scientific equipment that spins an object in a circle, applying a strong force running perpendicular to the axis of the spinning object. This creates centripetal acceleration.

Combustion chemistry: The chemical process of burning; oxidation and the generation of light and heat.

DNA and RNA: DNA stands for deoxyribonucleic acid; it is the molecule that contains genetic material, present in almost all living organisms. RNA stands for ribonucleic acid; it is a nucleic acid present in all living cells. Its major role is as the messenger carrying instructions from DNA for controlling the synthesis of proteins. Note: in some viruses RNA rather than DNA carries the genetic information.

Dot-com bubble: A stock market bubble (a situation where market prices are super, unsustainably high) fueled by investments in Internet-related companies in the late 1990s.

Embryo cells: These are the cells that come from the inner cell-mass of a blastocyst—an early-stage preimplantation embryo (the earliest stage in the development of fertilized egg).

Energy input: The amount of energy put *into* a device (whereas output is the amount of energy that comes *out*); for example, a light bulb's energy input is in the form of *electrical energy*, and its energy output is in the form of light/heat.

Enzyme: A substance made by a living organism; it works as a catalyst to a specific biochemical reaction.

Equity: the investment in stock shares.

GDP: Stands for Gross Domestic Product; it is the measure of added value (in other words, how much is) created through the production of goods/services in a country during a specific period.

Gene expression: The process by which the inheritable genetic information (the sequence of DNA base pairs) is turned into a "functional gene product" such as a protein.

Gene-splicing: The process by which an organism's DNA is cut, after which a gene (for example, from another organism) is inserted.

Genetic engineering: The changing of an organism's characteristics by manipulating its genetic material.

Genome: The set of chromosomes in an organism that makes up the whole of its hereditary information encoded in its DNA.

Genomics: The area of molecular biology that focuses on the structure, function, evolution, and mapping of genomes.

Human Growth Hormone: A peptide (a compound made up of 2+ amino acids) hormone that stimulates growth, cell reproduction, and cell regeneration.

Hydrogen Bubble chamber: A vessel filled with superheated liquid hydrogen; it is used to detect electrically charged particles moving through it.

In vitro fertilization: When eggs are extracted from a woman's ovary and combined with sperm outside the body—in test tubes (in vitro is Latin for "in glass")—to form embryos. The embryos are then grown in a lab, after which they're either put in a woman's uterus or frozen for later use.

Infrared spectrometer: A tool to measure and analyze of the interaction of infrared radiation (a type of electromagnetic radiation) with matter. It is used to study and identify the structure of chemical substances.

Insulin: A hormone that lowers the glucose (a type of sugar) level in the blood. It's made by the pancreas.

Isotopes: Variants of the atoms (tiny pieces of matter) of a chemical element (substance containing only one type of atom) which differ in neutron number, but contain the same number of protons (part of the atom found in the atom's nucleus) and electrons (negatively charged subatomic particles).

Mind-machine Interface: A direct communication pathway between an enhanced/wired brain and an external technological device.

Lymph nodes: A little bean-shaped organ that filters substances that travel through the body's lymphatic system (a network of thin, branching vessels); lymph nodes contain white blood cells, which help the body fight infection and disease.

Nasal polypectomy: A surgical procedure to remove polyps (soft growths that develop in the lining of the nose or sinuses).

Nucleic acid: Complex molecular substance present in living cells, especially DNA or RNA, where genetic information is stored.

Nucleoside: A compound found in DNA and RNA, containing of a five-carbon sugar as its base.

Nucleotide: A compound consisting of a nucleoside linked to a phosphate group (a chemical compound consisting of one phosphorus and four oxygen atoms, attached to a molecule containing carbon). Nucleotides form the basic structural unit of nucleic acids such as DNA.

Obstetrics and Gynecology: The medical branches that specialize in the care of women's reproductive systems and organs.

Pathogen: A bacterium, virus, or other microorganism that lead to or create disease.

Pharmacologists: Someone who specializes in the science of medications.

Photochemistry: The area of chemistry revolving around the chemical effects of light.

Photosynthesis: The process by which plants (and some other organisms) use sunlight to synthesize foods from carbon dioxide and water.

Plutonium: A radioactive chemical element.

Private sector: The part of the economy that is run by individuals and companies for profit and is not state or government controlled.

Protein synthesis: The two-stage process (transcription and translation) in which cells create proteins.

Recombinant DNA: DNA that has been made artificially by combining components from different organisms.

Ribosomal RNA: A type of non-coding RNA which is the primary component of ribosomes (the compounds that also include protein), essential to all cells. rRNA is a ribozyme, which carries out protein synthesis in ribosomes.

RNA polymerase: An enzyme that performs transcription (the process by which RNA is made from DNA).

Socratic dialogue: Named after the Greek philosopher Socrates, this method of communication involves a small group led by a facilitator—all of whom discuss a given topic critically and collaboratively, and by asking questions.

Spectroscopy: The area of science that focuses on the investigation and measurement of spectra (light and colors) produced when matter interacts with or emits electromagnetic radiation.

Stem cell research: The area of scientific inquiry that studies the stem cells (cells with the ability to develop into several types of cells in the body) and their potential use in medicine.

Sumatriptan pills: Medication used to treat migraine headaches.

Synergistic: Relating to the interaction or cooperation of 2+ substances to produce a combined effect greater than the sum of their separate effects.

Therapeutics: Medicine or treatment tools to help cure disease.

Tissue engineering: A biomedical field and process that modifies cells in order to restore, maintain or improve tissue function.

Venture capital: Capital (funds) invested in a project in which there is a high risk, typically with a new or expanding business.

Vietnam War: A conflict fought between North Vietnam (supported by the Soviet Union, China, and North Korea) and South Vietnam (supported by the Unites States, South Korea, Thailand, Australia, New Zealand, and the Philippines.) The war lasted almost 20 years.

Gallery of Superheroes

To my mind, nearly every person included in this book is heroic. Each made a dramatic impact on me—guiding or inspiring me in many ways toward a wonderful career in science.

The below collection is here so you can pick and choose who inspires *you*. Perhaps one day you will be assigned in school to write about a famous or influential person, describe an important historical event, or deeply explore something of your choosing in the world of science. Perhaps it won't even be for school; perhaps you're eager and excited right at this moment to dive deep and learn more about the lives of these magnificent individuals. So, behold! A final round-up of scientific stars—a gallery of men and women who are my superheroes:

***

Baruj Benacerraf: (1920 – 2011) President for several years of the outstanding cancer research and treatment center affiliated with Harvard Medical School, the Dana-Farber Cancer Institute. He was awarded a Nobel Prize for discoveries about the human immune system in 1980. He was a mentor of mine and one of my superheroes, not just for the legacy of knowledge he gave to the world but also for how he supported my own research efforts for treating HIV/AIDS.

Emmanuelle Charpentier: (1968 –) A French professor and researcher in microbiology, genetics, and biochemistry. She is best known for her work with Jennifer Doudna deciphering the molecular mechanisms of a bacterial immune system and repurposing it into a tool for genome editing, CRISPR-Cas9. She and Doudna, described below, are not only my personal superheroes, but they have also become global superheroes, having been awarded the 2020 Nobel Prize in Chemistry for their discovery.

Jennifer Doudna: (1964 –) An American biochemist best known for her discovery (with Emmanuelle Charpentier) of a molecular tool called CRISPR-Cas9, which provides the foundation for gene editing and making specific changes to DNA sequences. She and Charpentier were awarded the 2020 Nobel Prize in Chemistry for their discovery.

John Franklin Enders: (1897 – 1985) American biomedical scientist and Nobel Prize winner. He was the first with two colleagues in 1949 to demonstrate how to grow poliovirus in human muscle and tissue in a laboratory. This knowledge was essential for rapidly manufacturing vaccines to inoculate millions of people against polio in the 1950s and end that pandemic by the early 1960s. By giving me back my childhood freedom, he became a personal superhero to me.

Anthony Fauci: (1940 –) The Brooklyn-born doctor and scientist led the fight against infectious disease at the National Institutes of Health. He played a key role in the U.S. government's response to the AIDS pandemic, developing the program known as PEPFAR with President George W. Bush in Africa in 2003. Because of Fauci's hard work and dedication, millions of people in Africa and Caribbean countries have been spared once-fatal infections. Fauci has also been a leader in our efforts to confront COVID-19, becoming one the country's most trusted voices and most well known scientists.

Alexander Fleming: (1881 – 1955) Scottish physician and microbiologist best known for his discovery of penicillin, which is an antibiotic that can treat infections caused by bacteria, such as pneumonia, scarlet fever and infections of the ear, skin, gum, mouth and throat. Thanks to his keen powers of observation, he saved my life and hundreds of millions of others. He received the Nobel Prize in Physiology or Medicine in 1945.

Emil "Tom" Frei: (1924 – 2013) An American physician and distinguished cancer specialist, he pioneered the use of two or more drugs simultaneously and created the first cures for childhood leukemia. We later successfully applied this technique, known as combination chemotherapy, to treating AIDS patients.

James Watson: (1928 –) Watson along with research colleague Francis Crick discovered the double helix structure for DNA in a Cambridge University lab in England in 1953. This was one of the great scientific achievements of all time, the modern basis for the exciting new field of molecular biology. Watson and Crick shared the Nobel Prize in 1962. With his book, *Molecular Biology of the Gene*, he laid the foundation for modern biomedical science.

Li Wenliang: (1986-2020) Li was an ophthalmologist who was among the first to warn the world about the outbreak of COVID-19. Initially, hu=I swarningsm met with skepticibi but turned out LI was right. His courage in speaking out about the outbreak early, saved countless lives. Unfortunately, shortly after he warned the world about the new disease, he became infected while treating one of his patients. In early February 2020 Li passed away from complications due to COVID-19. He was a true hero, until the very end.

Acknowledgments

T he number of people I have to thank for this book are too varied and numerous to mention, from my classmates and friends on the deserts of China Lake, to the colleagues and friends I have worked with over the years in classrooms, laboratories and offices around the world.

I would especially like to thank my former Harvard colleagues in the department of HIV/AIDS research and the department of human retrovirology research, many of whom continue to find solutions for some of the most important infectious disease and public health challenges facing the world today. I thank them not only for the work they have done and continue to do, but also for their efforts to preserve and expand upon the knowledge they have gained by cultivating and training new generations of young scientists.

As always, I am tremendously grateful to my loving wife, Maria Eugenia, my children Mara and Alexander, my stepdaughters Karina, Manuela and Camila, and my grandchildren Pedro, Enrique and Carlos for the joy and happiness they have brought to my life.

And finally—and most importantly!—to you, my readers (including two young readers, Neala and Willa, who helped choose some of the images in this book), I offer you my debt of thanks. Someone once said heroes are made by the path they choose, not the powers they are graced with. Your curiosity, your interest, and your love of learning is already making the world a better place, in ways big and small. Never forget it…the fate of our world is in your good hands.

CPSIA information can be obtained
at www.ICGtesting.com
Printed in the USA
LVHW071331190621
690651LV00009B/295